Number Crunchers

Mind Bogglers

Also in the Number Crunchers series

Brain Bafflers

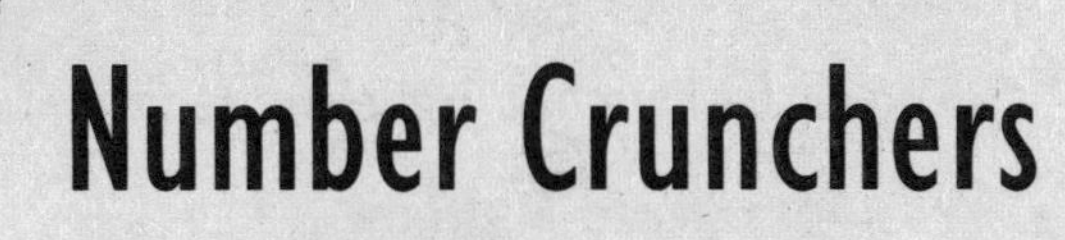

Number Crunchers

Mind Boggler

Rowland Morgan

MACMILLAN CHILDREN'S BOOKS

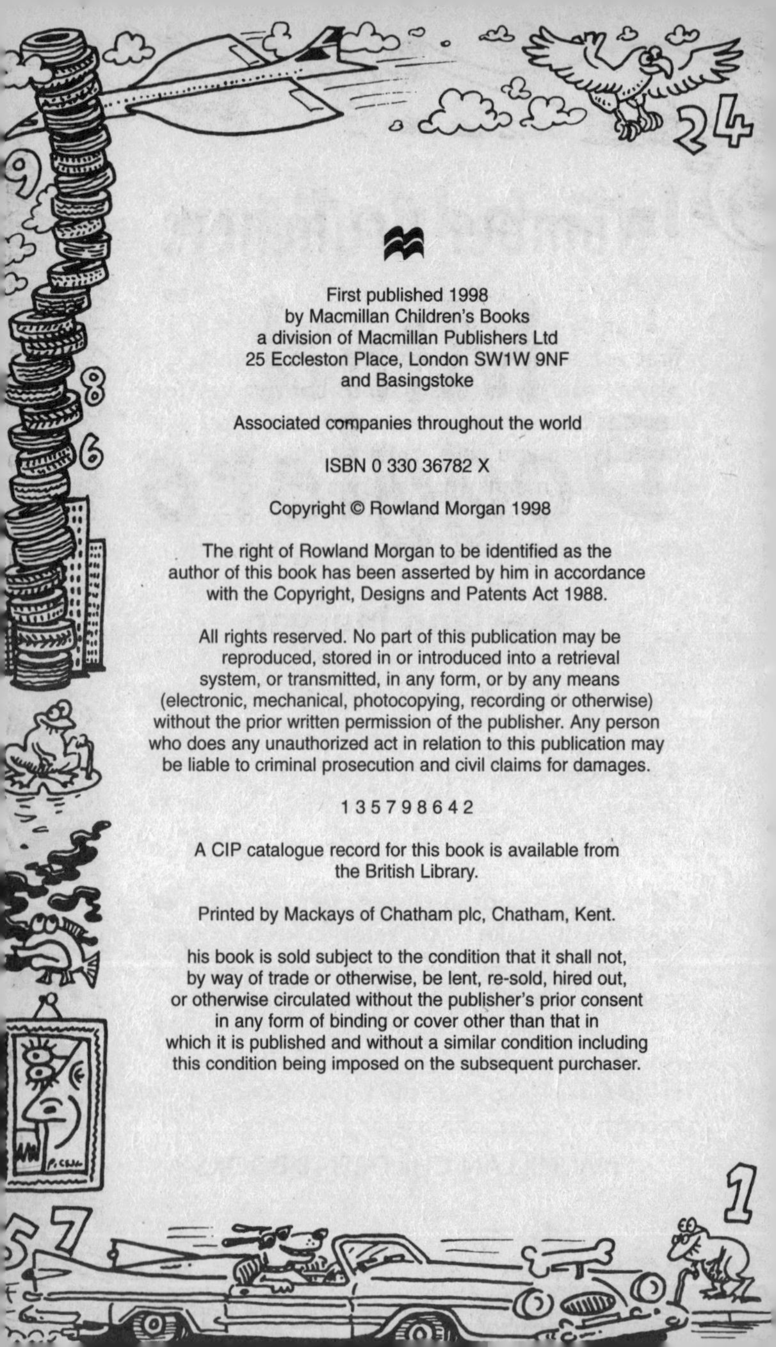

First published 1998
by Macmillan Children's Books
a division of Macmillan Publishers Ltd
25 Eccleston Place, London SW1W 9NF
and Basingstoke

Associated companies throughout the world

ISBN 0 330 36782 X

1 3 5 7 9 8 6 4 2

A CIP catalogue record for this book is available from
the British Library.

Printed by Mackays of Chatham plc, Chatham, Kent.

Introduction

You don't have to be a rocket scientist to enjoy working out mind-boggling facts. I first got a grip on mental arithmetic while playing darts, which is a subtracting game. You start at 301 and subtract every score you make. Then you have to end with a double to win, which means working out that, for example, if your score is 25, you need one of the following combinations to reach exactly zero:

1 and 12 + 12
or
3 and 11 + 11
or
5 and 10 + 10
or
7 and 9 + 9 (and so on).

Of course, it's not just your own calculations you have to make – you want to keep an eye on your opponent's as well – so darts keeps you surprisingly busy at mental arithmetic.

Another game with lots of arithmetic is cricket. Take a look at the book of cricket records, *Wisden*, one day, and you'll see that

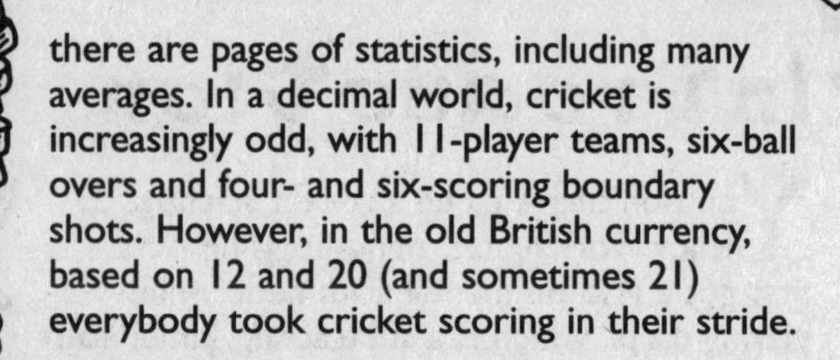

there are pages of statistics, including many averages. In a decimal world, cricket is increasingly odd, with 11-player teams, six-ball overs and four- and six-scoring boundary shots. However, in the old British currency, based on 12 and 20 (and sometimes 21) everybody took cricket scoring in their stride.

Another game with plenty of mental arithmetic is ten-pin bowling. First, you should work out how much it costs to play per hour. It would also be interesting to find out the electricity consumption and global warming involved. If you can afford a game, you'll have to grapple with 'strikes' and 'spares' and the fairly complicated numbering carry-overs involved.

Computers

Numbers are spreading, and the reason is the computer. It is worth remembering that most people in the world have never seen one, let alone used one. A typical desktop computer uses as much power as two powerful traditional light bulbs. If you worked a desktop computer with bicycle pedals, you would have to cycle at full speed, pedalling uphill all the time. Production is huge: every working day in Taiwan alone, factories produce a stack of notebook computers 59 storeys high, or nearly as high as Britain's tallest building (Canary Wharf tower). The 84,000 desktop computers at the Hewlett Packard computer company require the power of 21 electric trains. You can work out that the world's computers use nearly as much electricity as Brazil.

World computer electricity consumption per year in kilowatt hours: 240,000 million
Kilowatt hours used in Brazil: 249,000 million
249,000 – 240,000 = 9,000

Computers can 'read' numbers, using a laser beam to decipher a bar-code. Few products are without a bar-code today. Basically, the code is a series of eleven numbers made up of groups of 0's and 1's (in other words, they are 'digital'). The scanner goes across the black and white bars of the code and 'reads' a dark strip as 0 and a white strip as 1. (A bar can be thin, if it has only one strip, or thicker if it has two or more strips side by side). As well as the coded numbers, there are edge markers, a centre marker, and an extra number that is used for checking for errors. There's an easy way to find a sample bar-code: just look at the back of this book.

An interesting mind-blower about computers. If transistors in computer chips keep growing

in power at a consistent rate, computers 50 years from now will be 100,000 times more powerful. I wonder if they could write this book automatically?

Internet Numbers

About 20 million computers are linked into the wide-area network called the Internet. You have probably seen an Internet address (URL for short), which identifies a website, which is a primitive TV channel. For example: http://www.macmillan.co.uk is the website address of this book's publisher. However, that is only an 'outer' address. It actually stands for, guess what, another number. There is a building near Washington DC which contains a stack of powerful 'server' computers which instantly convert the millions of internet addresses into numbers for computer processing. In 1997 there was a breakdown, and the whole worldwide web collapsed, causing horror and dismay in the business world. If you'd like to e-mail me, my address is: rrmorgan@netcomuk.co.uk

Mind-Bogglers

Quite simple calculations can have a nice big effect when you try them out on people. For example, if the subject of sleep comes up, you might mention that we are asleep more than four months of each year. It means that if we live for another, say, 60 years, we will sleep for:

60 x 4 = 240 (months)
240 ÷ 12 = 20

an astounding twenty years.

You can cite a mind-blower worked out from what is probably the most famous mathematical formula: Albert Einstein's $E = mc^2$. The formula illustrates that if some way is found to convert mass into energy, there is a huge multiplication factor (c^2), the square of the speed of light. It means that, for example, if a cake weighing 0.45 kilograms could all be converted into energy, it would generate about 11 billion kilowatt hours, which could power 30,000 colour TV sets every evening (4 hours) for the next 1,000 years. That's quite a cake!

Here's one about your brain. Everybody's got one (or should have). An American expert worked out that the brain makes about 1,000 million million operations per second. If computers keep growing in power at their current rate, they should be able to match

that by 2050. It means you could have a strap-on brain that recalls everything you read, hear and see, while you stare out of the window and dream.

The Big Number

We inhabit a world in which the biggest feature is no longer a bomb, but a number. It's the imminent doubling of our human population to about 10 thousand million. The astonishing fact is, that if everybody had about one square metre each, that whole doubled population of the world could stand in the county of Devon. If they had the space we enjoy in Britain, they would only require Asia. The rest of the continents could be empty. If they lived everywhere, they would only have the density enjoyed by the French. And, if they shared out the five continents equally, everybody would have a plot the size of a football field. If you got part of the Sahara desert you could rent it out for solar power, and if you got a peak in the Himalayas, maybe you could sell the water.
Happy number crunching!

This book contains 78 number crunchings that I've done for you. The statistics I used are provided in a Statpak. If the fact is laid out as a multiple choice, you can guess the right

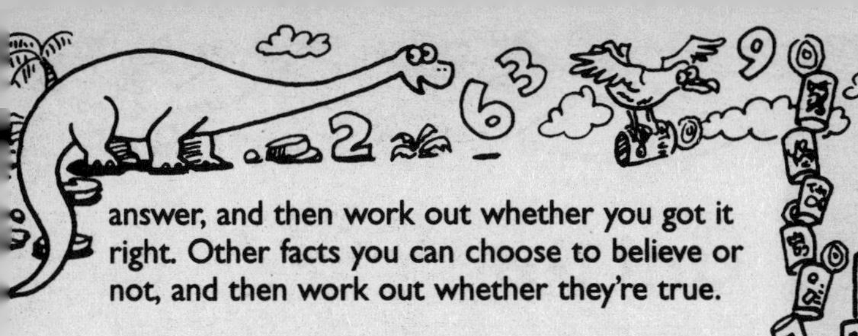

answer, and then work out whether you got it right. Other facts you can choose to believe or not, and then work out whether they're true.

A note on huge numbers

Like the world's human population, numbers are getting bigger all the time. Your calculator will probably handle eight figures, that means a maximum of 99,999,999. If you are calculating billions (1,000,000,000, also known as a thousand million) you may need to drop one set of noughts, as in the following operation:

7,001,000 (000) ÷ 365 = 19,180 (000) =
19,180,000 ÷ 2,300,000 = 8.339

In order to fit the billions in, you drop three noughts, and add them on as soon as they will fit onto the LCD screen. In the above operation, you add them on in the second calculation.

Rounding: numbers rounded up, or down, are shown in brackets, or after an equals sign like this: 48.9 = 50.

Units

To express today's huge statistics in a way that is easier to picture than strings of figures, we use big visual units. Here's a list of the main ones with their facts and figures.

Unit List

SUPERTANKER

Load: 100,000 tonnes

The world fleet of supertankers is approximately 800. Three thousand smaller tankers have a combined cargo capacity of 263 million tonnes. The total tanker fleet capacity is about 360m tonnes.

JUGGERNAUT LORRY

Average load: 23 tonnes

16 metres long

There are 79,000 38-tonne articulated lorries in Britain. They could jam up a six-lane motorway for 210 kilometres, or 130 miles, further than London to Birmingham. They can carry between 20 and 24 tonnes of freight.

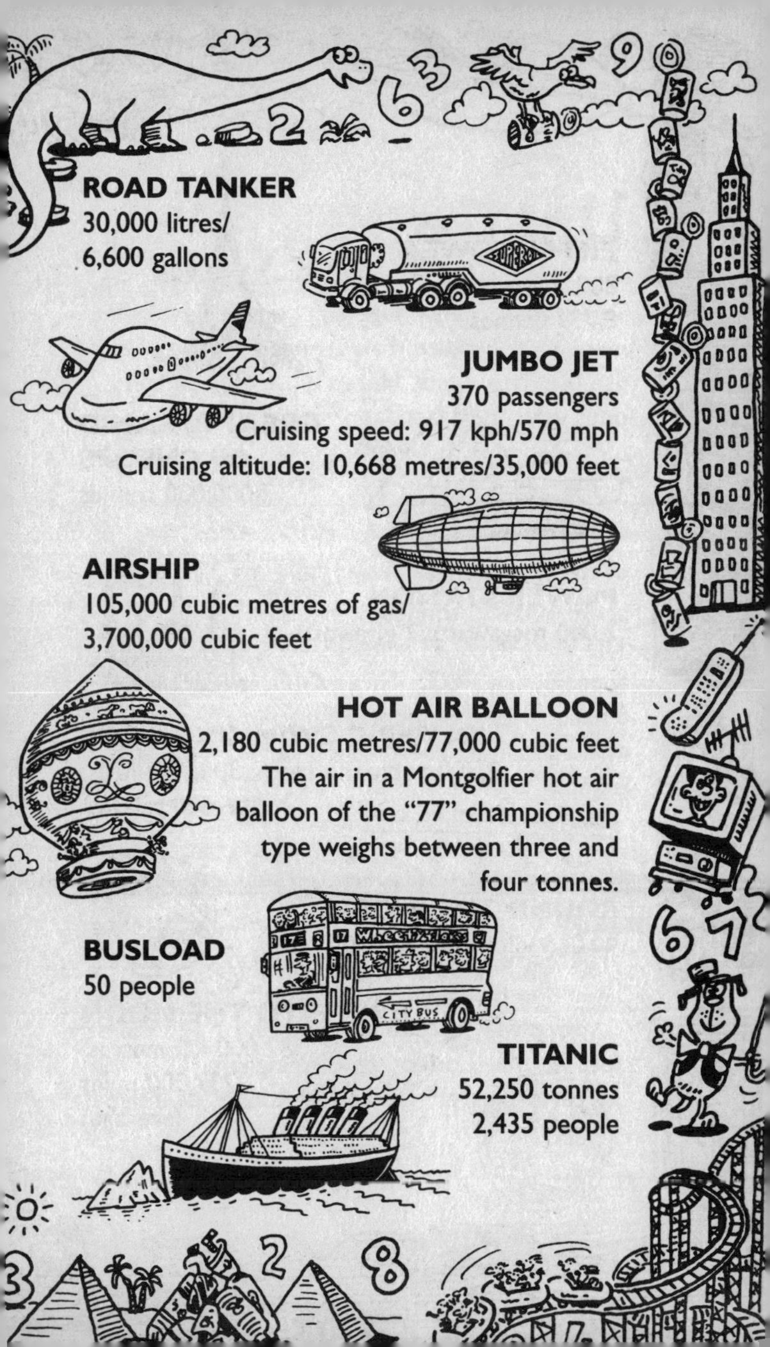

ROAD TANKER
30,000 litres/
6,600 gallons

JUMBO JET
370 passengers
Cruising speed: 917 kph/570 mph
Cruising altitude: 10,668 metres/35,000 feet

AIRSHIP
105,000 cubic metres of gas/
3,700,000 cubic feet

HOT AIR BALLOON
2,180 cubic metres/77,000 cubic feet
The air in a Montgolfier hot air balloon of the "77" championship type weighs between three and four tonnes.

BUSLOAD
50 people

TITANIC
52,250 tonnes
2,435 people

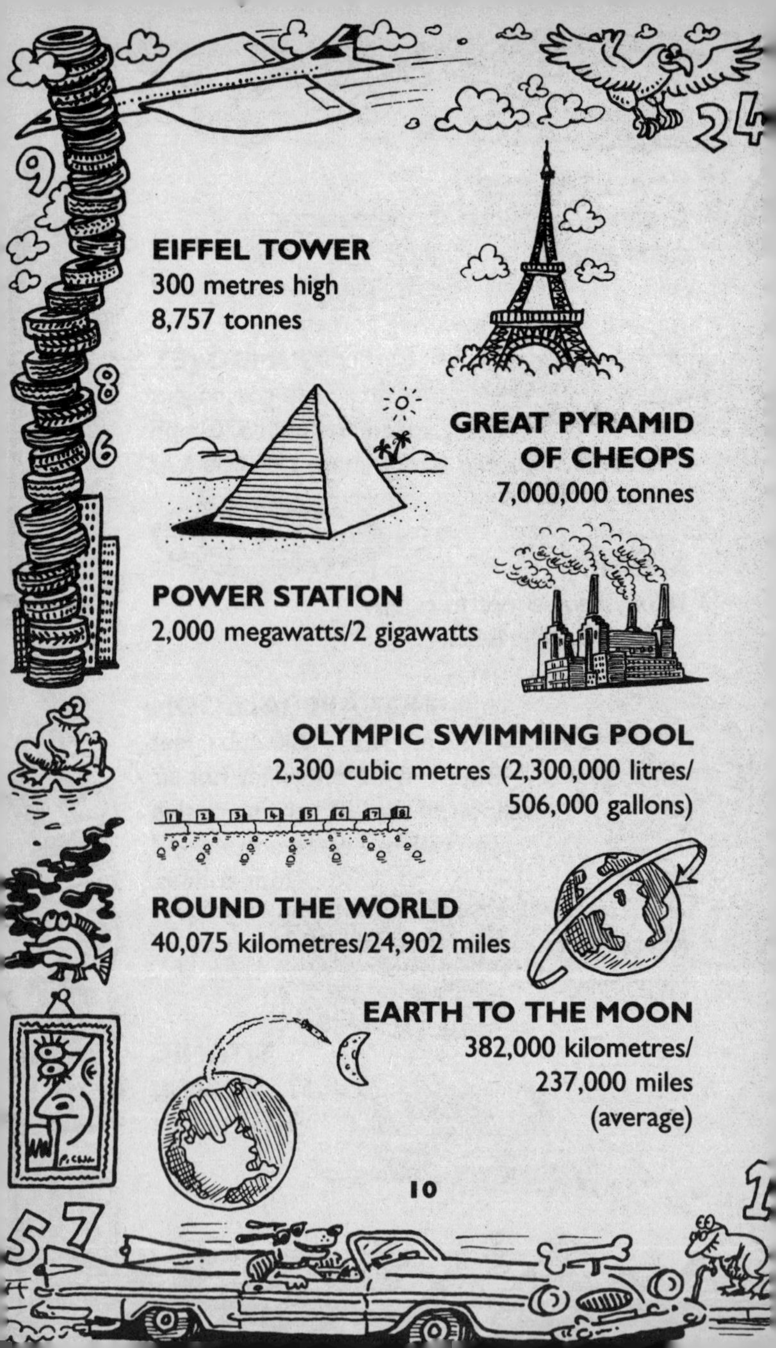

EIFFEL TOWER
300 metres high
8,757 tonnes

GREAT PYRAMID OF CHEOPS
7,000,000 tonnes

POWER STATION
2,000 megawatts/2 gigawatts

OLYMPIC SWIMMING POOL
2,300 cubic metres (2,300,000 litres/ 506,000 gallons)

ROUND THE WORLD
40,075 kilometres/24,902 miles

EARTH TO THE MOON
382,000 kilometres/ 237,000 miles (average)

Percentage increase per year

Companies always want to sell you more, so they are forever measuring percentage increases. A useful trick for finding out how many years it will take for an amount to double is to divide its annual percentage increase into 70. So, a five per cent annual increase means that the annual amount will double in 70 ÷ 5 = 14 years.

A note on your calculator

The mind-blowers in this book are for crunching numbers, not brains. They are meant to blow minds, not fuses. A standard calculator will do. You need not worry about a GCSE calculator or A-level calculator. If you are using an advanced calculator, you will have to remember the BODMAS formula which governs the order in which calculations are made.

Believe it? Or not?

Boys and girls made into human sacrifices by Aztec priests in ancient Mexico could have filled Wembley Stadium 40 times.

Statpak

Boys and girls estimated to have been made into human sacrifices by Aztec priests in Mexico: 4,000,000
Wembley stadium capacity: 100,000

Michael Tobias, Environmental Meditations

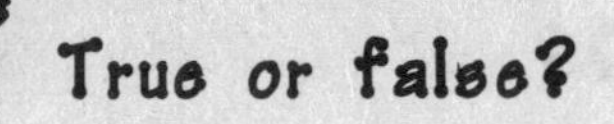

True or false?

The largest mammal on Earth is 70,000,000 times bigger than the smallest.

Statpak

Grams weighed by the smallest shrew: 2
Tonnes weighed by the largest whale: 140

The Hutchinson Dictionary of Science

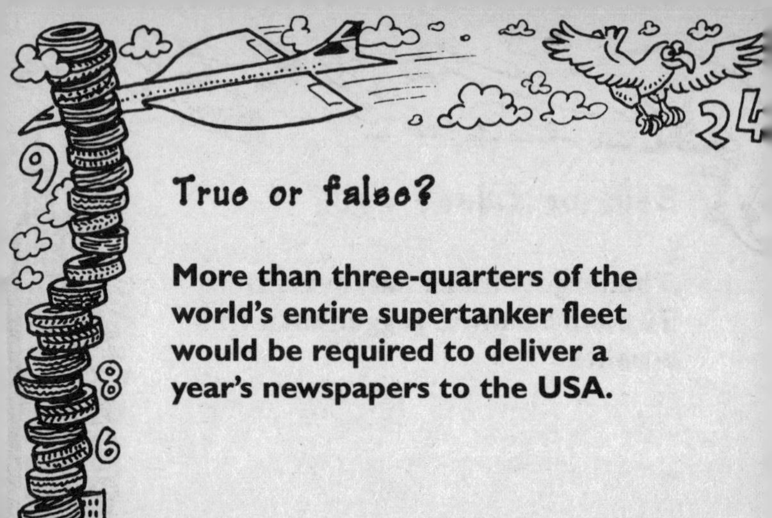

True or false?

More than three-quarters of the world's entire supertanker fleet would be required to deliver a year's newspapers to the USA.

Statpak

World supertanker fleet (over 100,000 tonnes capacity): 791
Capacity of supertanker: 100,000 tonnes
Tonnes of newspapers recycled by Americans each year: 18,960,000
Tonnes of newspapers dumped by Americans each year: 47,536,000

National Geographic vol 186 no 1

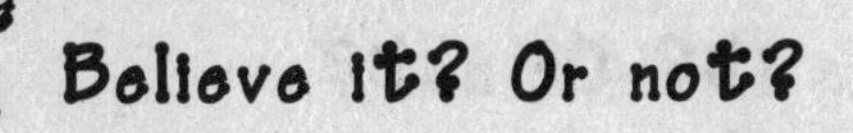

Believe it? Or not?

About 117,000 human lives could be lived during a year's British TV viewing.

Statpak

Average daily hours' TV viewing: 3.5
British population: 58,000,000
Hours in average lifetime: 630,000

BFI Film & TV Handbook

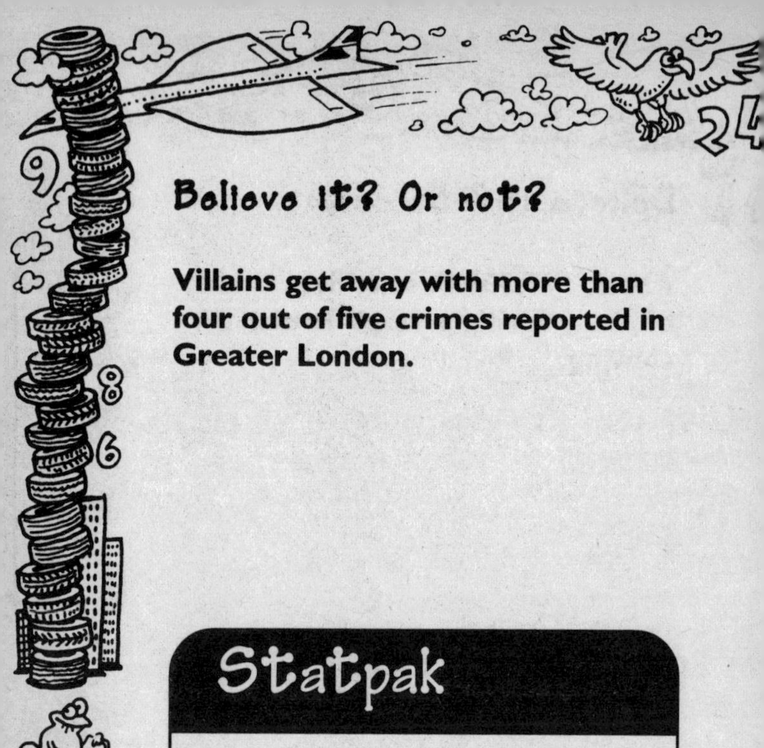

Believe it? Or not?

Villains get away with more than four out of five crimes reported in Greater London.

Statpak

Reported crimes per year: 944,185
Cleared up by police: 150,946

Metropolitan Police Commissioner's Annual Report

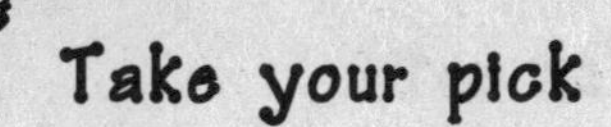

Take your pick

The area of Earth's surface that is water could accommodate Europe

1) 3
2) 5
3) 35

times.

Statpak

Area of planet Earth's surface: 509,953,886 square kilometres
Percentage of Earth's surface that is water (including polar ice caps): 71
Area of Europe: 10,400,000 square kilometres

Focus magazine

Take your pick

A glass of bottled mineral water costs

1) 1.5
2) 15
3) 15,000

times more than a glass of tapwater.

Statpak

Cost of a glass of tapwater: 0.001p
Of a glass of mineral water from a supermarket: 15p

The Water Companies Association/ The Times (1.5 litres of mineral water @ 75p; 300cl glass)

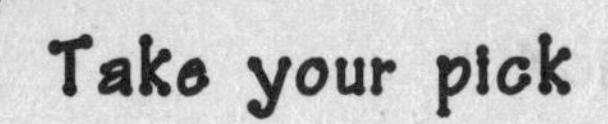

Take your pick

Out of 10 new British aluminium cans,

1) one
2) two
3) seven

are littered, or thrown onto the rubbish dump.

Statpak

Aluminium cans littered or sent to landfill: 4,300,000,000
Recycled: 1,200,000,000

Aluminium Can Recycling Association (1993)

Take your pick

Japanese shoppers spend

1) 18
2) 180
3) 1,800

times more than shoppers in Ghana.

Statpak

An average Ghanaian spends $5 a year in the shops, a Japanese: $9,000

Euromonitor International Marketing Data & Statistics

Take your pick

North Americans use

1) twice
2) three times
3) 300 times

more petrol than residents of India.

Statpak

Tonnes of petrol used by an average American per year: 1.25
By an average Indian: 0.004

Euromonitor International Marketing & Statistics

True or false?

Residents of Sussex lived without cars for 20,000 generations.

Statpak

Date of human tibia bone found buried in Boxgrove, Sussex: 498,000 BC
Date of mass motoring in Sussex: 1960–70 AD
Years in one generation: 25

Geographical LXVI no 7

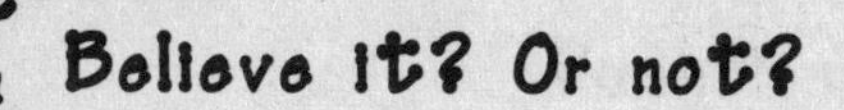

Shipping away a year of all waste generated by modern Britons would require a nose-to-tail queue of juggernauts stretching six times round the globe.

Statpak

Waste generated by modern Britons per year: 400,000,000 tonnes
Juggernaut load: 23 tonnes
Length of juggernaut: 16 metres
Circumference of Earth at the equator: 40,075 kilometres (24,902 miles)

Ministry of Agriculture, Fisheries & Food

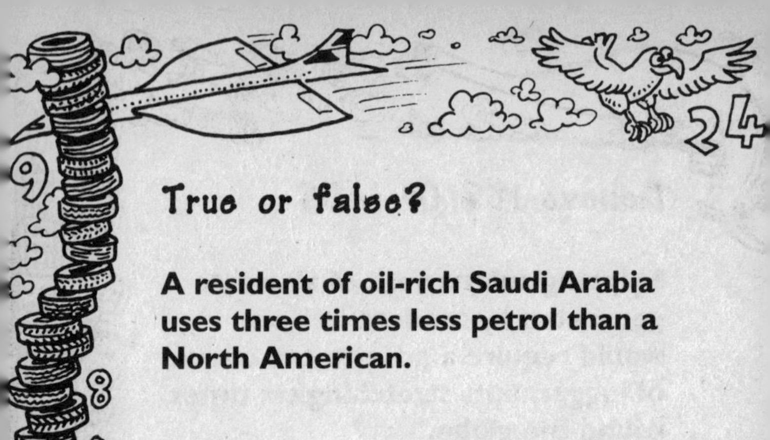

True or false?

A resident of oil-rich Saudi Arabia uses three times less petrol than a North American.

Statpak

Tonnes of petrol used annually per Saudi Arabian: 0.376
Per North American: 1.25

Euromonitor International Marketing Data & Statistics

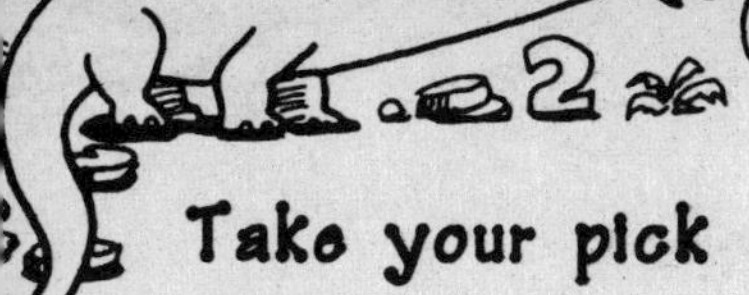

Take your pick

Americans dump

1) 1
2) 3
3) 11

supertankers of paper a week.

Statpak

Supertanker-loads of paper Americans make a year: 771
Supertanker-loads they recycle or export for recycling: 220

National Geographic vol 186 no 1

True or false?

A heavy object dropped into the ocean over the Mariana Trench in the Pacific would take over one hour to sink to the bottom.

Statpak

Deepest part of Marianas Trench in the Pacific Ocean: 11,034 metres (36,201 feet)
Speed at which a heavy object sinks: 10 kilometres per hour (6.2 miles per hour)

The Hutchinson Dictionary of Science

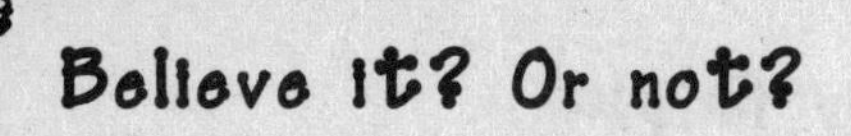

Believe it? Or not?

Only 20 years of production would be required to string a line of Barbie Dolls to the Moon.

Statpak

Centimetres per Barbie: 30 (12 inches)
Annual Barbie-brand doll production: 63,000,000
Moon's average distance from Earth: 382,000 kilometres (237,000 miles)

Mattel Corp

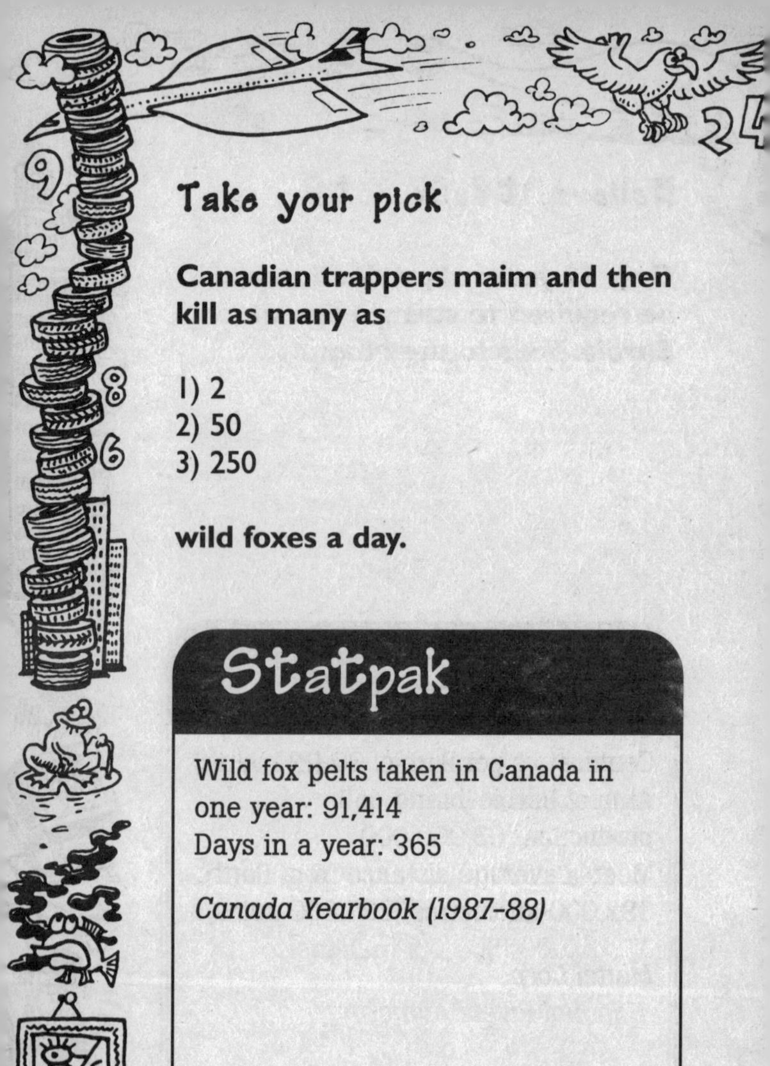

Take your pick

Canadian trappers maim and then kill as many as

1) 2
2) 50
3) 250

wild foxes a day.

Statpak

Wild fox pelts taken in Canada in one year: 91,414
Days in a year: 365

Canada Yearbook (1987-88)

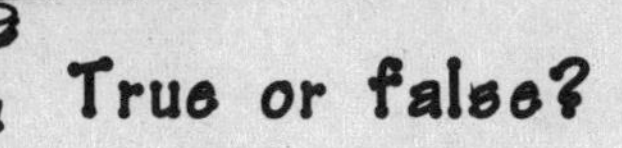

True or false?

Sewers dump nearly 400 Olympic pools of untreated sewage onto British shores every day.

Statpak

Litres of untreated sewage discharged at coastal outlets per day:
909,091,000 (200,000,000 gallons)
Litres in an Olympic swimming pool:
2,300,000 (506,000 gallons)

National Rivers Authority

Take your pick

Britons watch about

1) 2
2) 23
3) 23,000

years of TV a night.

Statpak

Typical hours of daily viewing: 3.5
Days in year: 365
UK population: 58,000,000

British Audience Research Board (BARB)

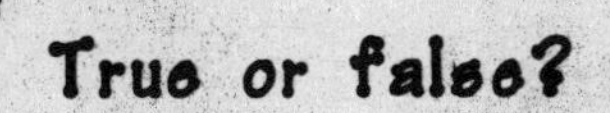

True or false?

Plastic junked by Americans every year weighs more than two Great Pyramids of Cheops.

Statpak

Weight of plastic consumed every year by Americans: 15,000,000 tonnes
Weight of plastic recycled each year by Americans: 363,000 tonnes
Pyramid: see page 10

National Geographic vol 186 no 1

Take your pick

It would take a typical stage play

1) 1
2) 11
3) 118

years to reach one Coronation Street audience.

Statpak

Average attendance at a live modern drama production: 381
Theatre performances per year: 364
Typical measured TV audience of Coronation Street: 16,350,000

Society of London Theatre, Independent London (7 performances per week) /Broadcast magazine

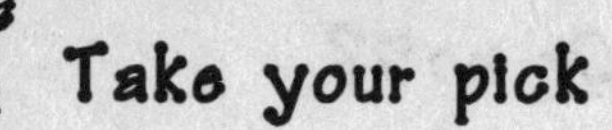

Take your pick

Over

1) 280
2) 28,000
3) 28 million

American children do not live in traditional two-parent families.

Statpak

Percentage of US children not living in traditional two-parent families:
49.2

Americans under the age of 15:
58,300,000

The Economist/San Francisco Chronicle/Microsoft Bookshelf

Believe it? Or not?

Oil spills polluting the oceans each year are the equivalent of nine major supertanker disasters.

Statpak

Estimated tonnes of oil spilled on the oceans each year: 2,000,000
Tonnes of oil spilled on Brittany's coast by the supertanker Amoco Cadiz: 223,000

Focus magazine/Chambers Catastrophes & Disasters

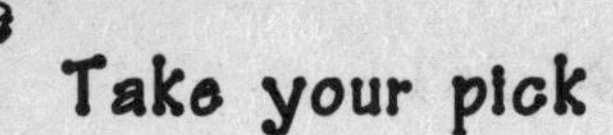

Take your pick

Coca-Cola spends over

1) £1,000
2) £10,000
3) £1 million

a month advertising sugar and water.

Statpak

Percentage of Coca-Cola that is sugar and water: 99.5
One month's Coca-Cola advertising budget: £1,025,000

New Statesman & Society/ Marketing Week

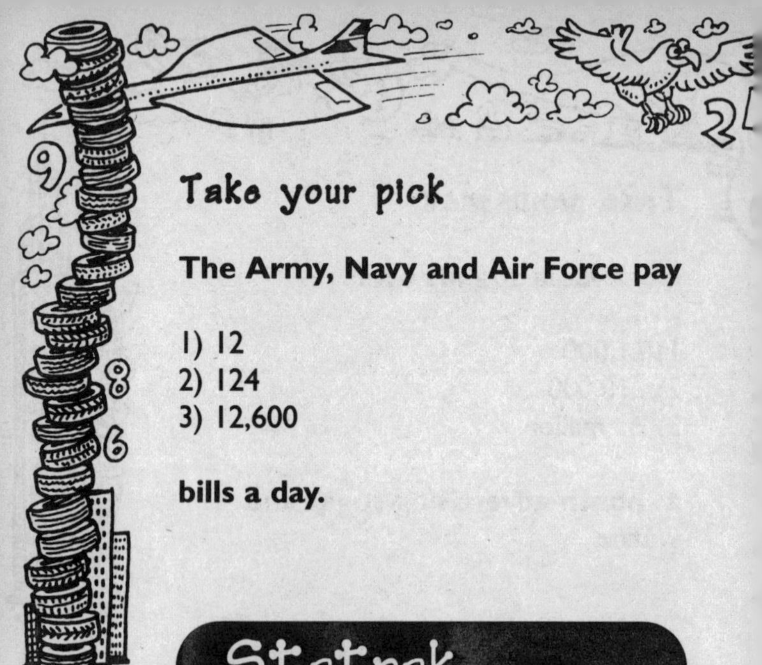

Take your pick

The Army, Navy and Air Force pay

1) 12
2) 124
3) 12,600

bills a day.

Statpak

Bills paid per year by the Ministry of Defence: 3,300,000
Working days per year: 260

Hansard vol 246 no 135 col 632

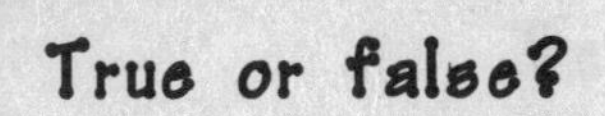

True or false?

Each day's weather forecast costs more than a quarter of a million pounds.

Statpak

Annual spending of the Meteorological Office: £93,200,000
Days in the year: 365

Hansard vol 246 no 135 col 631

True or false?

The English wiped out wolves more than 600 years before the French did.

Statpak

Year extermination programme finally wiped out English wolves: 1290

Year last wolf seen in France: 1929

Wolf Watch UK

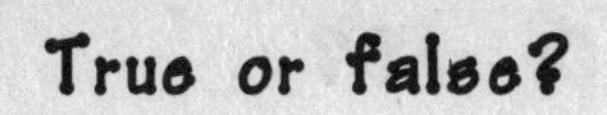

Seven million people in Bombay, India, live in slums, with as many as 30 people to a room.

Statpak

Percentage of Bombay's population living in slums: 50
Population of Bombay (also called Mumbai): 14 million

BBC News & Current Affairs

Believe it? Or not?

A Hollywood performing dog earns as much in two days as a typical resident of Haiti does in a year.

Statpak

Hollywood per day rate of a performing dog: $200
Annual per capita income of a Haitian: $400

Variety/ Latin America Outlook

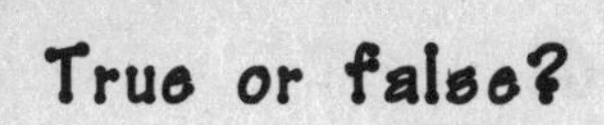

True or false?

Britain fought World War 2 with a million fewer telephones than are now carried in people's pockets.

Statpak

Cellular telephones registered: 4,000,000
Telephone stations in 1937-38: 3,000,000

British Telecom/Whitaker's Almanack for 1939

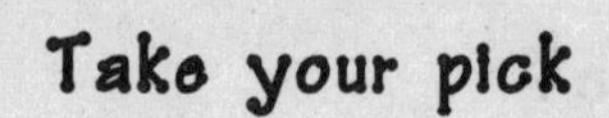

Take your pick

A day's water supply for holiday-playground Florida, USA, could be delivered by the river Amazon in:

1) one week
2) one day
3) eight minutes

Statpak

Amazon flow: 33,000,000 gallons per second
Florida's daily water consumption: 17,000,000,000 gallons

Quid

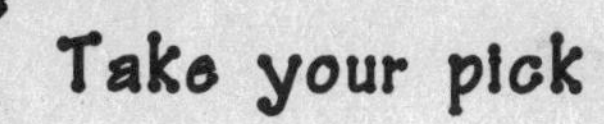

Take your pick

A keen driver could test-drive a different new car model every Saturday for:

1) three weeks
2) six months
3) 14 years

Statpak

Varieties of car on sale in Britain: 750
Saturdays in a year: 52

Top Gear BBC2-TV

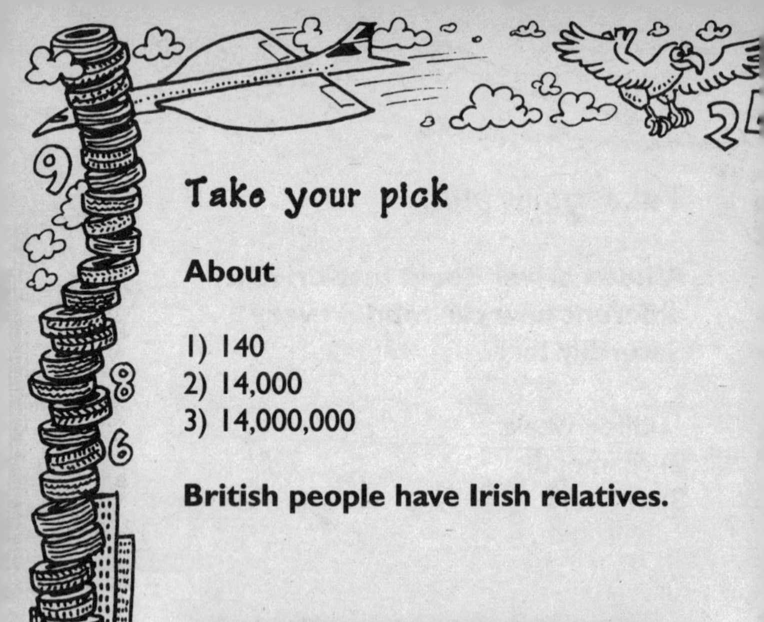

Take your pick

About

1) 140
2) 14,000
3) 14,000,000

British people have Irish relatives.

Statpak

Percentage of the British with Irish relatives: 24
Population of Britain: 58,000,000

ICM/University of Bradford

Take your pick

Round the clock, Britons are consuming nearly two bath-tubs of sugary soft drinks every:

1) hour
2) minute
3) second

Statpak

Capacity of bath-tub: 150 litres
Consumption of soft drinks per year: 9,000,000,000 litres

The Grocer

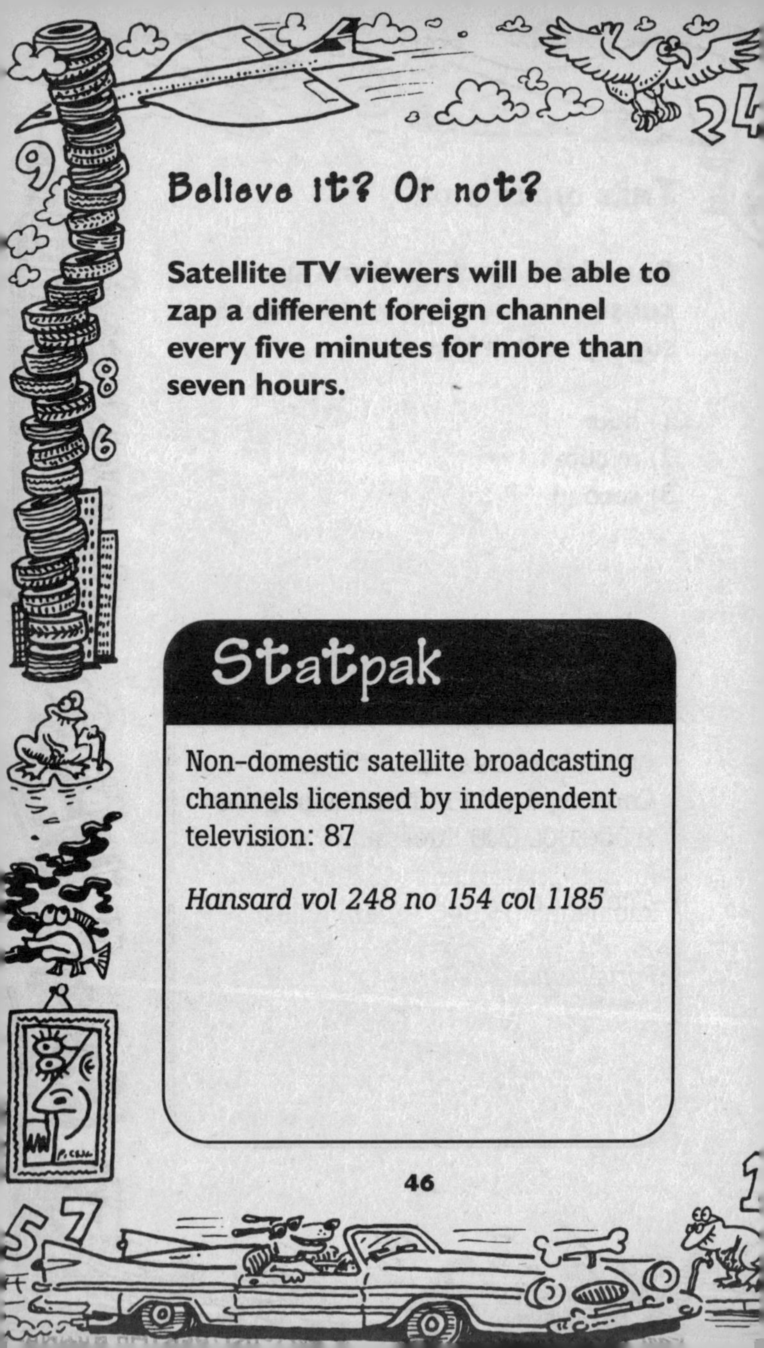

Believe it? Or not?

Satellite TV viewers will be able to zap a different foreign channel every five minutes for more than seven hours.

Statpak

Non-domestic satellite broadcasting channels licensed by independent television: 87

Hansard vol 248 no 154 col 1185

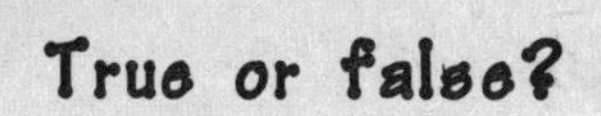

True or false?

Each surviving lynx in France has an area bigger than Switzerland to live in.

Statpak

Lynx left in France: 10
Area of France: 543,965 square kilometres (209,970 square miles)
Area of Switzerland: 41,300 square kilometres (15,946 square miles)

Paris Match 2372

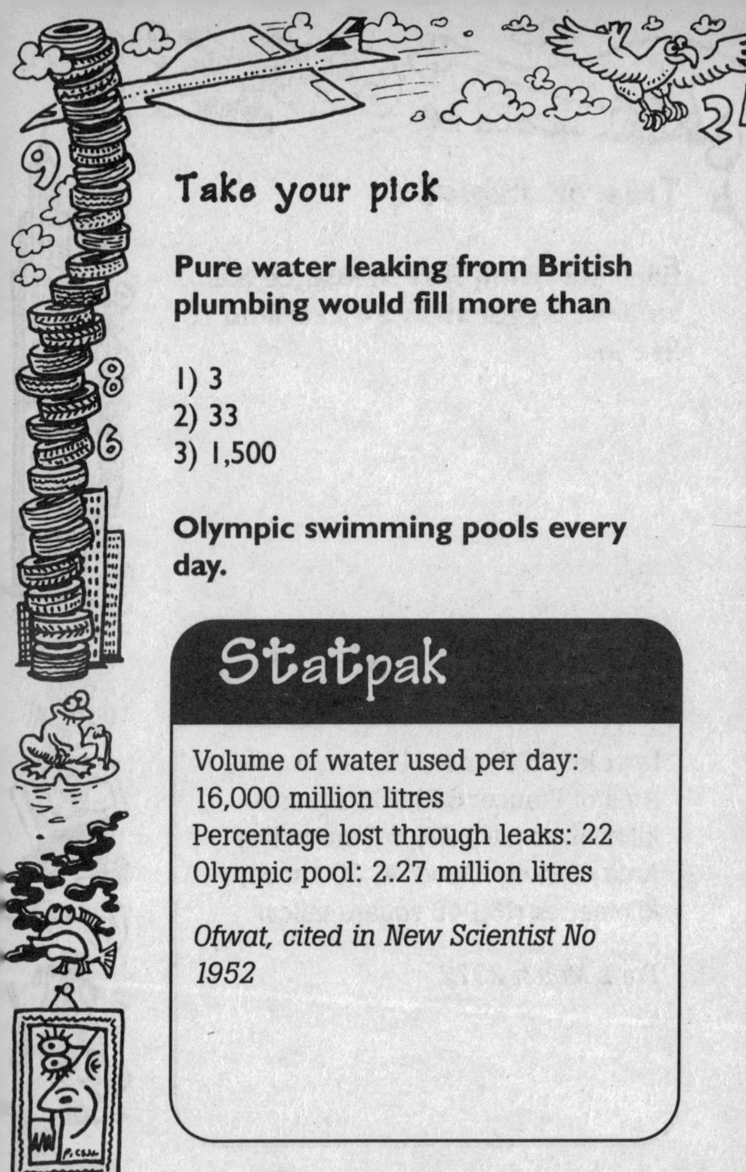

Take your pick

Pure water leaking from British plumbing would fill more than

1) 3
2) 33
3) 1,500

Olympic swimming pools every day.

Statpak

Volume of water used per day: 16,000 million litres
Percentage lost through leaks: 22
Olympic pool: 2.27 million litres

Ofwat, cited in New Scientist No 1952

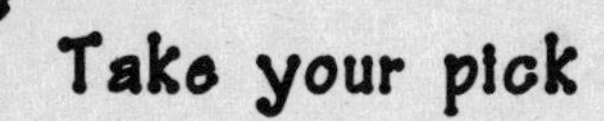

Take your pick

Each surviving royal eagle couple in France has a living area the size of nearly

1) one
2) two
3) 179

Lancashires.

Statpak

Couples of royal eagles estimated left in France: 100
Area of France: 543,965 square kilometres (209,970 square miles)
Area of Lancashire: 3,040 square kilometres (1,173 square miles)

Paris Match 2372

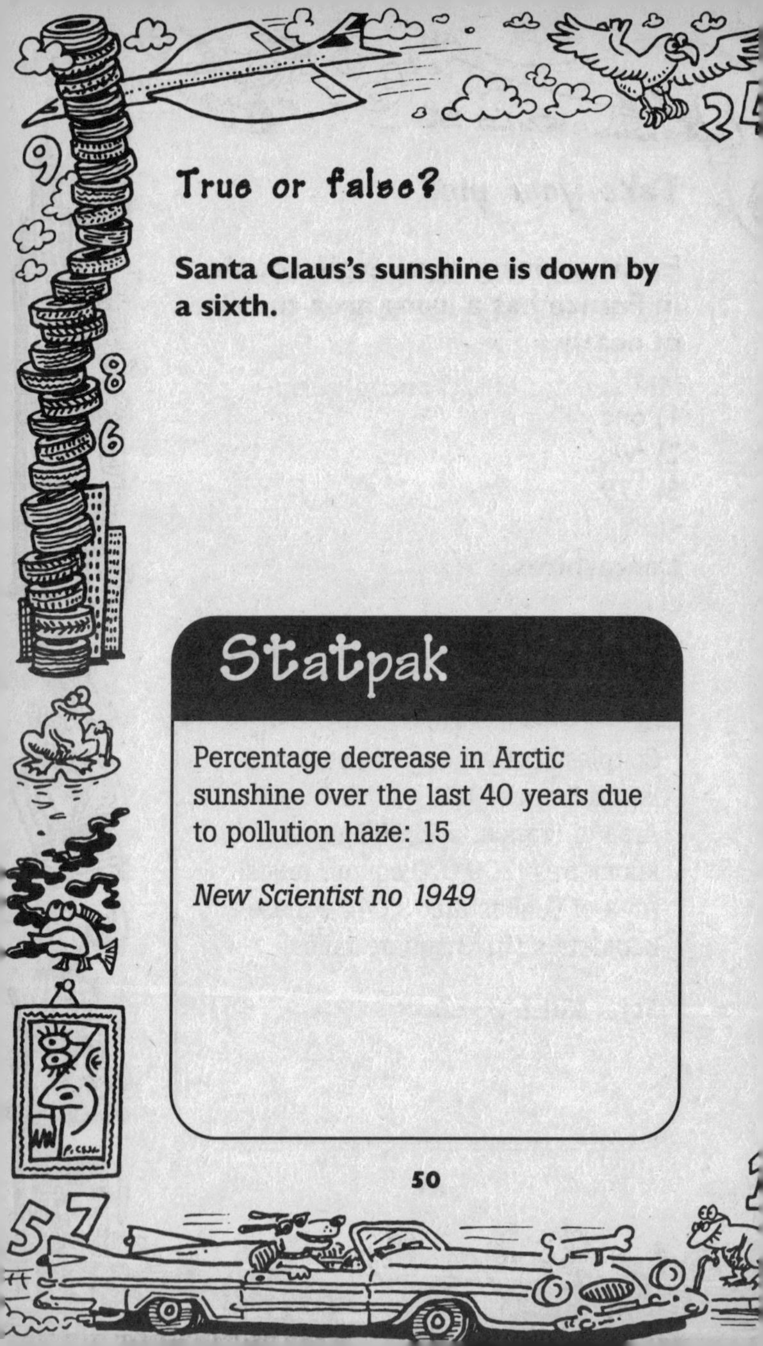

True or false?

Santa Claus's sunshine is down by a sixth.

Statpak

Percentage decrease in Arctic sunshine over the last 40 years due to pollution haze: 15

New Scientist no 1949

Take your pick

Cars to fill the car park at one of the world's biggest shopping centres, the Mall of America, in Minnesota, USA, could queue

1) 5
2) 10
3) 58

kilometres to get in.

Statpak

Parking spaces at the Mall of America: 12,750
Average length of car: 4.6 metres

Focus the Magazine of Discovery

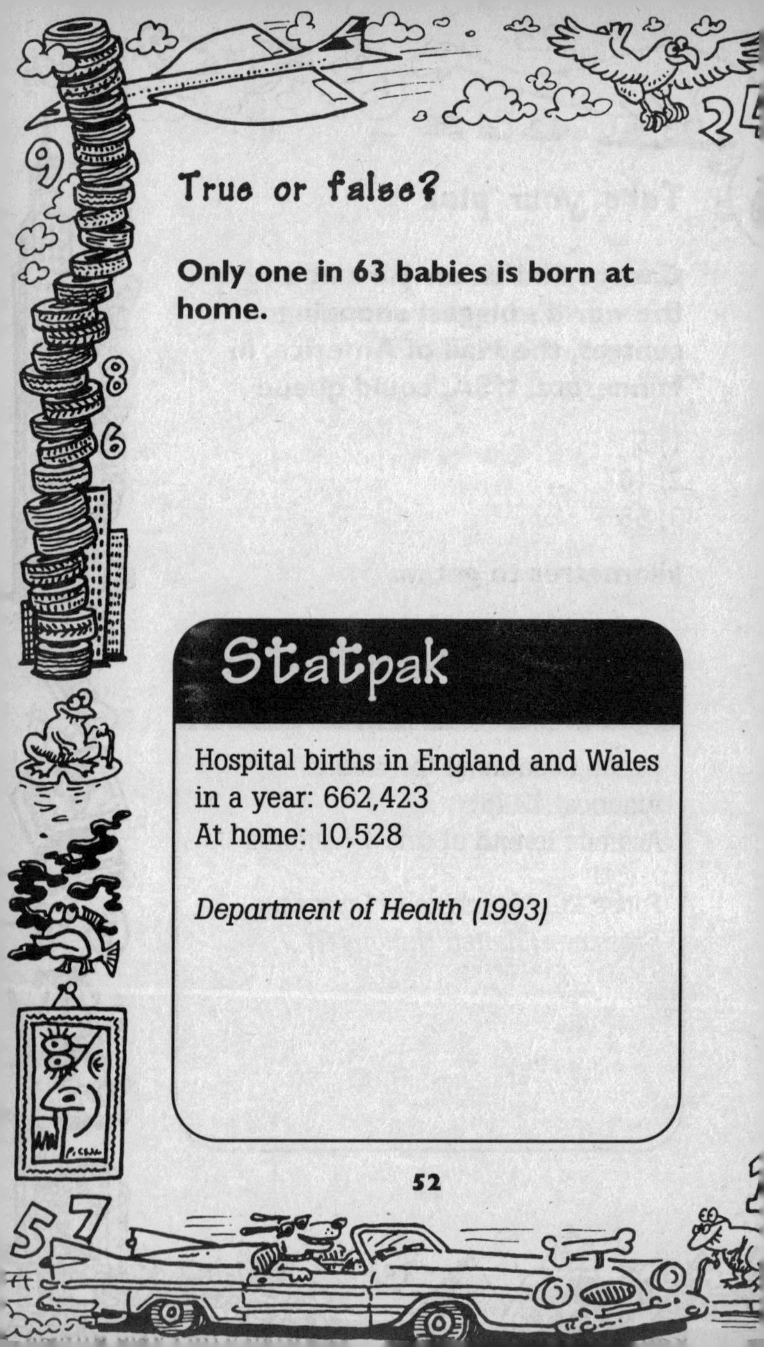

True or false?

Only one in 63 babies is born at home.

Statpak

Hospital births in England and Wales in a year: 662,423
At home: 10,528

Department of Health (1993)

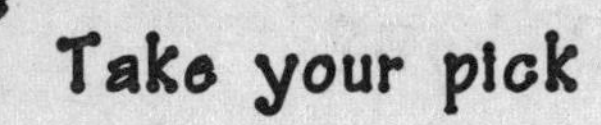

Take your pick

A forgotten landmine could explode somewhere every hour of every day for over

1) 1.1
2) 11
3) 11,000

years.

Statpak

Unexploded mines buried across the world: 100,000,000
Days in a year: 365

Crosslines/United Nations

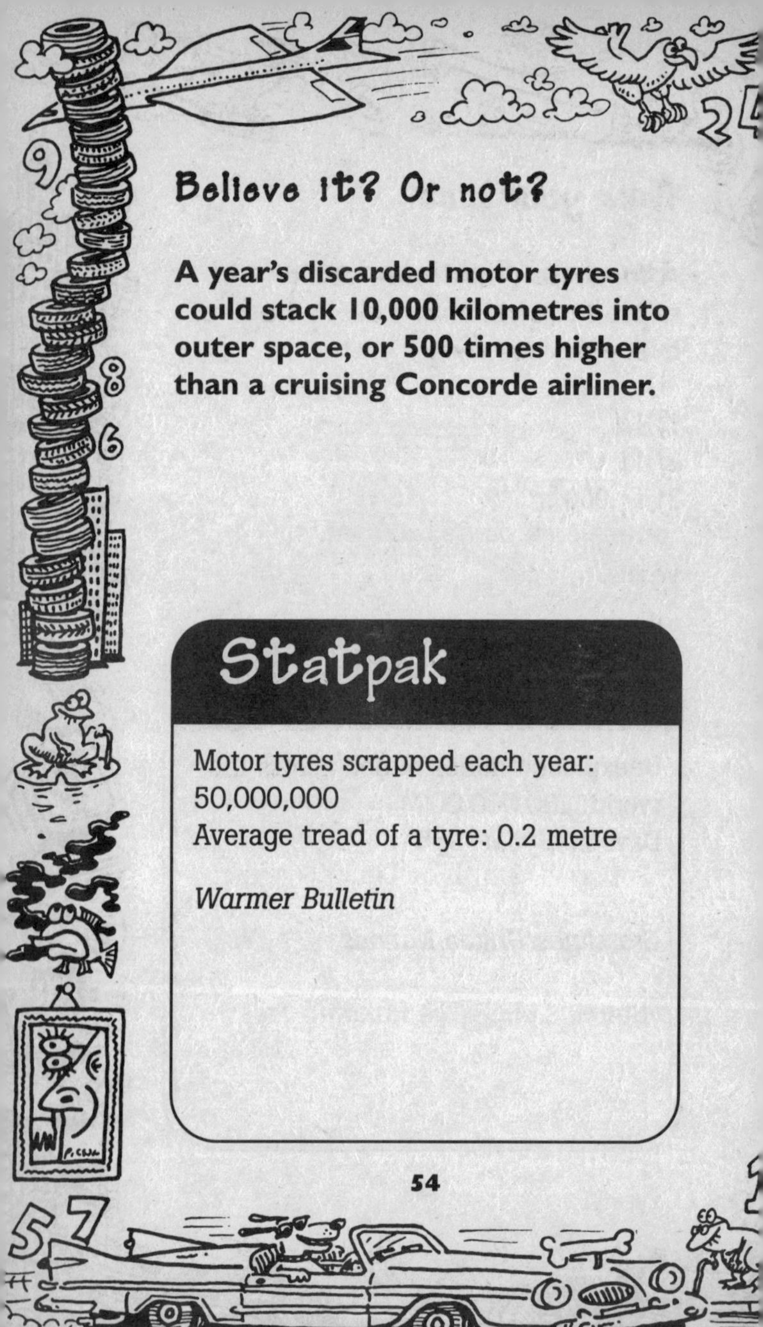

Believe it? Or not?

A year's discarded motor tyres could stack 10,000 kilometres into outer space, or 500 times higher than a cruising Concorde airliner.

Statpak

Motor tyres scrapped each year:
50,000,000
Average tread of a tyre: 0.2 metre

Warmer Bulletin

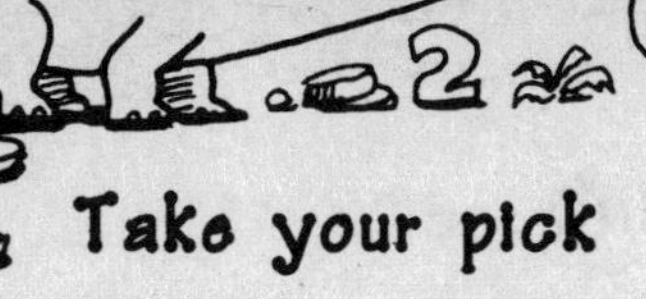

Take your pick

Henry the Eighth had an average of

1) 1
2) 2
3) 5

enemies a day executed.

Statpak

Persons estimated to have been put to death on the orders of King Henry the Eighth: 72,000
Period of Henry the Eighth's reign: 1509–1547
Days in a year: 365

Gatrell, V.A.C., The Hanging Tree

Take your pick

Sugar added to UK processed foods each year could fill:

1) two vans
2) two juggernauts
3) two supertankers

Statpak

Tonnes of sugar added to UK processed foods: 200,000
Supertanker load: 100,000 tonnes

Nature vol 373 no 6514

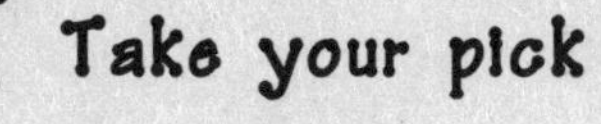

Take your pick

A rail trip by a member of the royal family costs

1) 3
2) 6
3) 6,300

times more than the average.

Statpak

Average cost of a journey by royals: £19,101
By a member of the public in normal railcars: £3.00

Dept of Transport (45 trips in 1994 costing £2 million)/BR Press Office

True or false?

In the next three minutes, a stack of bottles and jars over four times higher than Mount Snowdon will be dumped on the British isles.

Statpak

Bottles and jars thrown away annually: 6,000,000,000
Average height of bottles & jars: 0.15 metres
Days in a year: 365
Hours in a day: 24
Height of Mount Snowdon: 1,085 metres (3,560 ft)

Centre for Alternative Technology

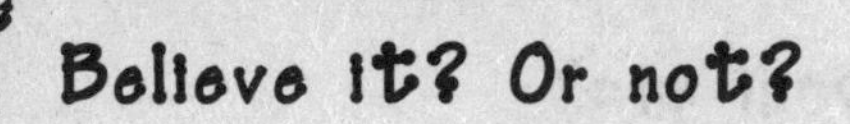

Believe it? Or not?

A total jam-up of every lane of every motorway in Britain could accommodate only one in four motor vehicles.

Statpak

Metres of motorway lane:
19,000,000 (62.4 million feet)
Metres of vehicles: 76,000,000 (251 million feet)

Whitaker's Almanack (vehicle 10ft)

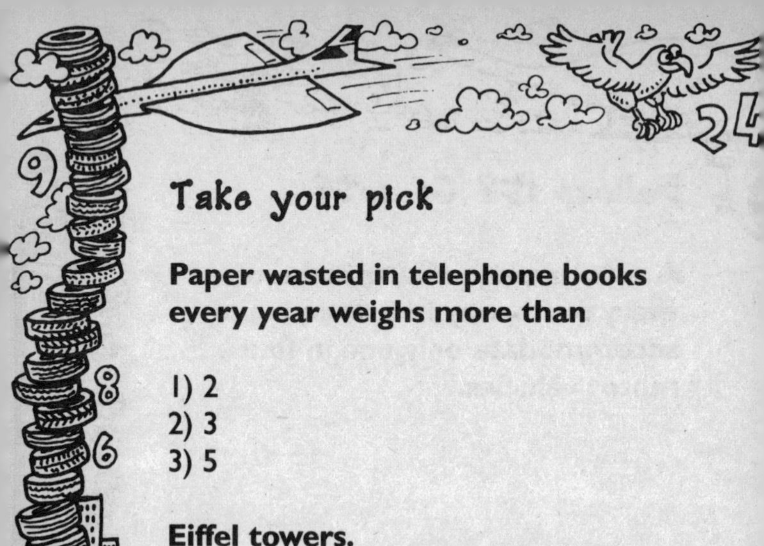

Take your pick

Paper wasted in telephone books every year weighs more than

1) 2
2) 3
3) 5

Eiffel towers.

Statpak

Tonnes of phone books published per year: 57,576
Percentage of recycled fibre used: 20
Weight of the Eiffel Tower: 8,757 tonnes

BT and the Environment

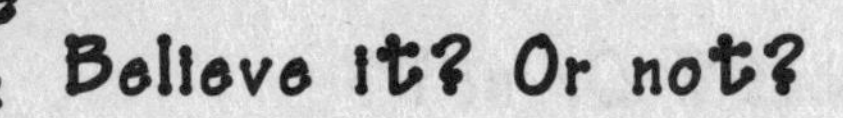

A night in prison costs 30 per cent more than a night in a Mayfair hotel.

Statpak

Average cost of a night's detention in a police cell: £289
Price of a night at London's Dorchester Hotel: £215

Home Office Hansard vol 263 no 133 col 284/Dorchester Hotel

Believe it? Or not?

On a given day, thieves steal only one car in 15,000.

Statpak

Average daily car thefts: 1,683
Private and light goods vehicles: 25,000,000

Home Office Hansard 235/25 col 272

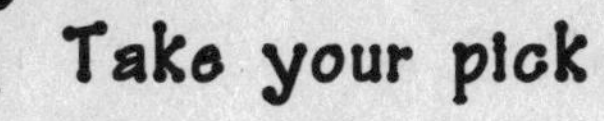

Take your pick

An overdue £15 cassette at a video shop costs

1) 2
3) 5
3) 70

times more a than an overdue £15 book at a public library.

Statpak

Daily fine on an overdue book at a West London public library: £0.05
On an overdue overnight cassette at a West London video outlet: £3.50

Blockbuster/Richmond Upon Thames

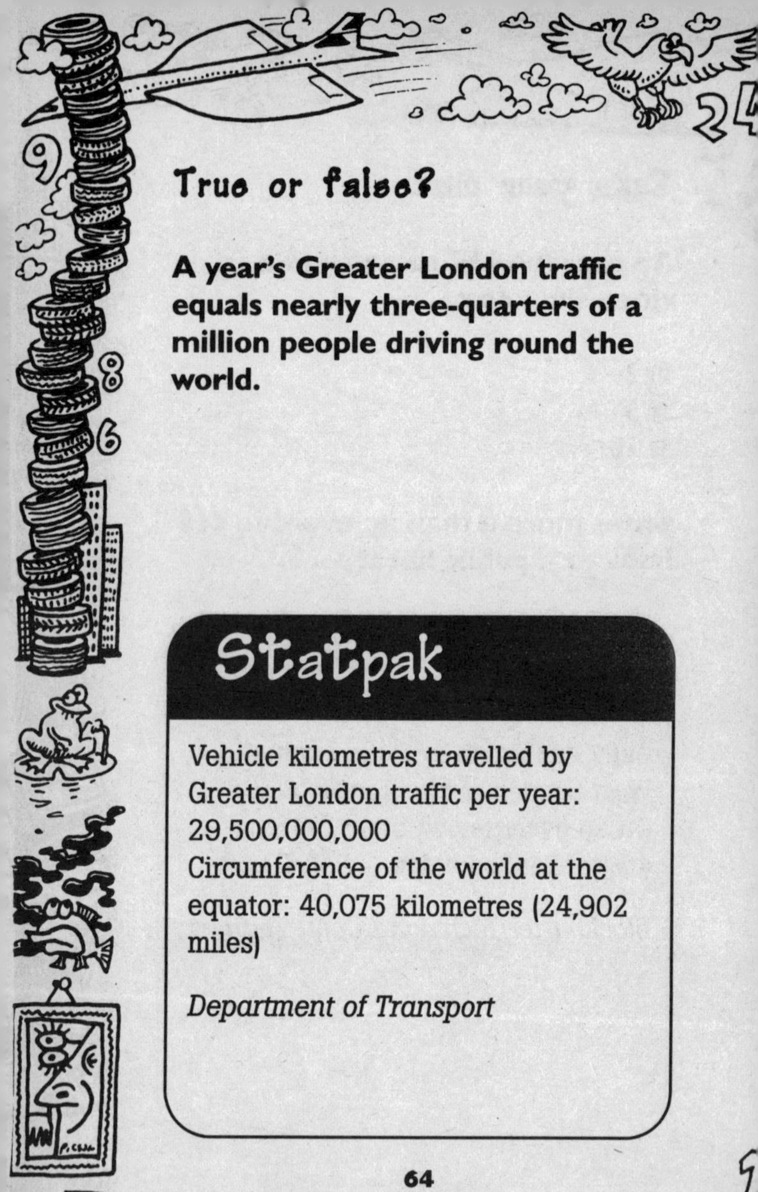

True or false?

A year's Greater London traffic equals nearly three-quarters of a million people driving round the world.

Statpak

Vehicle kilometres travelled by Greater London traffic per year: 29,500,000,000
Circumference of the world at the equator: 40,075 kilometres (24,902 miles)

Department of Transport

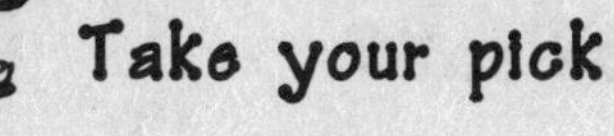

Take your pick

The electricity used by one car factory could power

1) 2
2) 4
3) 40

railway trains.

Statpak

Wattage of Toyota's Burnaston car plant: 40 million
Wattage required per train on the East coast main line: 1 million

Powergen advertisement/Railtrack

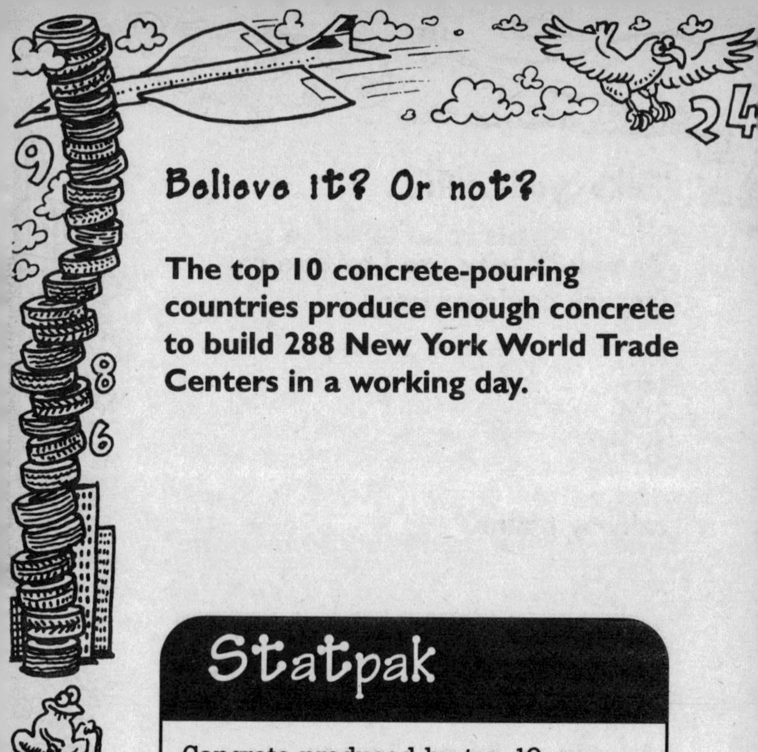

Believe it? Or not?

The top 10 concrete-pouring countries produce enough concrete to build 288 New York World Trade Centers in a working day.

Statpak

Concrete produced by top 10 countries per year: 877,000,000 tonnes
Concrete in World Trade Center towers: 12,127 tonnes
Working days in a year: 251

Quid

Take your pick

Collecting his robe of office from the Pope in 990 AD, Archbishop Sigeric took six months to make the journey from Canterbury to Rome, which was

1) 3
2) 100
3) 2,500

times slower than it could be done today.

Statpak

Air kilometres from London to Rome: 1,440 (895 air miles)
Airbus cruising speed: 853 kilometres per hour (530 miles per hour)

Chronicle of Britain

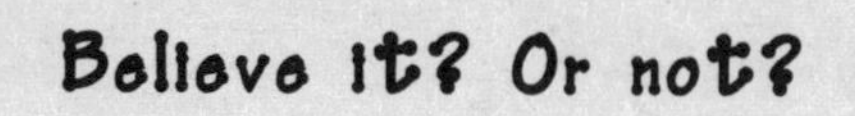

Believe it? Or not?

The frog has been a successful species on Earth for between 950 and 1,900 times longer than homo sapiens.

Statpak

Fossil-proven age of the frog: 190 million
Estimated age of homo sapiens: 100,000–200,000

New Scientist No 1995/The Cambridge Encyclopedia

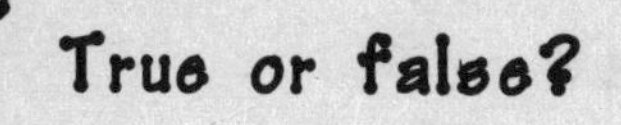

True or false?

Four weddings and a funeral would cost about £35,000.

Statpak

Average cost of a wedding: £8,500
Of a funeral: over £1,000

Freedom's Children/The Natural Death Centre

True or false?

The artist Pablo Picasso averaged over eight hand-made pictures every day of his 75-year adult life.

Statpak

Days in Picasso's adult life: 27,375
Paintings, drawing and engravings of Picasso: 240,000

Chronicle of the 20th Century

Take your pick

There are

1) 1 million
2) 10 million
3) 100 million

more Brazilians now than when the Queen was crowned.

Statpak

Population of Brazil in 1953: 52,840,000
In 1997: 155,000,000

Business Education Network

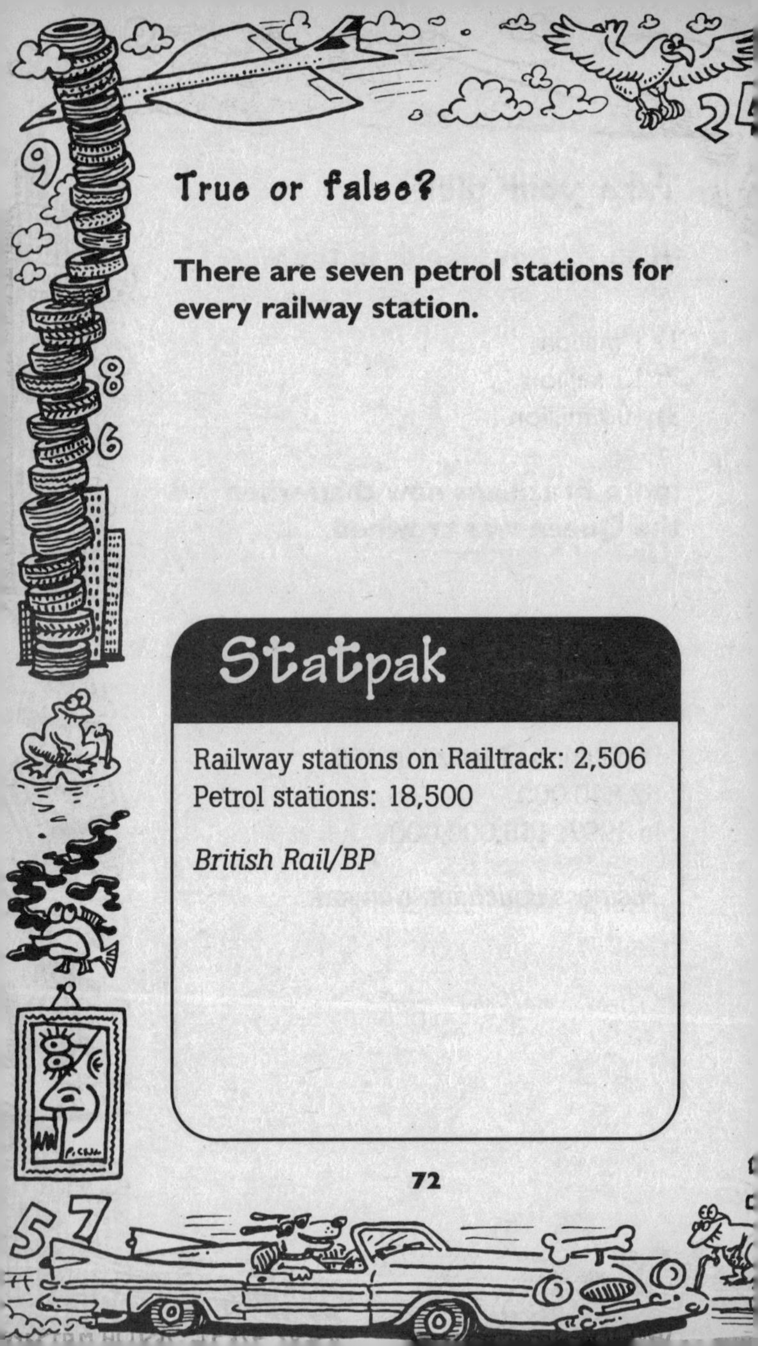

True or false?

There are seven petrol stations for every railway station.

Statpak

Railway stations on Railtrack: 2,506
Petrol stations: 18,500

British Rail/BP

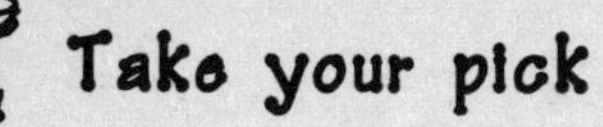

Take your pick

If all TV households in the world switched on an electric toaster, it would require the power capacity of

1) 2
2) 20
3) 18

United Kingdoms.

Statpak

Estimated TV households: 800,000,000
UK electricity capacity: 64,400 million watts
Toaster power consumption: 1,500 watts

The Times/Powergen

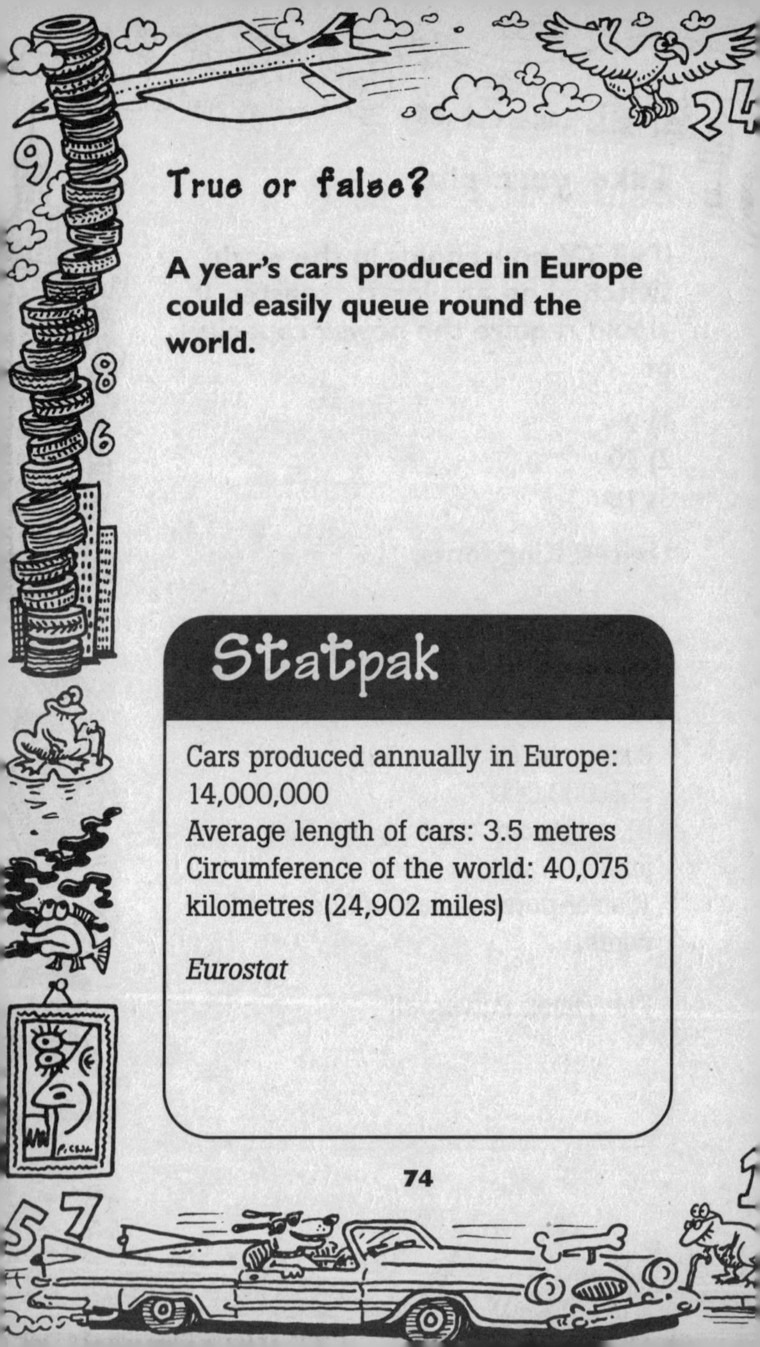

True or false?

A year's cars produced in Europe could easily queue round the world.

Statpak

Cars produced annually in Europe: 14,000,000
Average length of cars: 3.5 metres
Circumference of the world: 40,075 kilometres (24,902 miles)

Eurostat

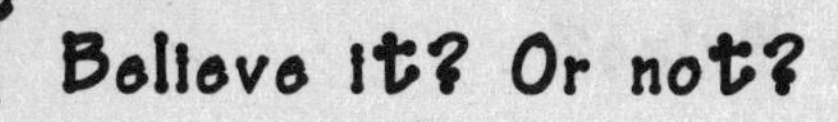

Believe it? Or not?

American roads cover a bigger area than England.

Statpak

Hectares of roads in the USA: 15 million
Hectares of England: 13 million

Wackernagel & Rees, Our Ecological Footprint

True or false?

Each working day, 26 football fields of English rural land get built up.

Statpak

English land built on each year: 6,800 hectares
Football field area: 1 hectare
Working days in a year: 261

Indicators of Sustainable Development, Dept of the Environment

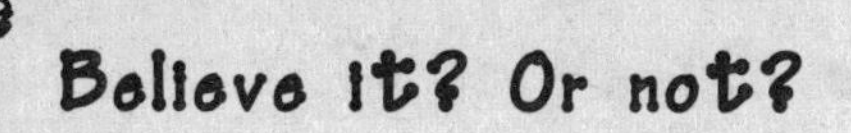

Believe it? Or not?

You could stand the world population in the county of Devon.

Statpak

Area of Devon: 6,720,000,000 square metres (8,037,037,037 square yards)
Estimated world population: 5,700,000,000

The Hutchinson Guide to the World/Cohen, J., How Many People Can The Earth Support?

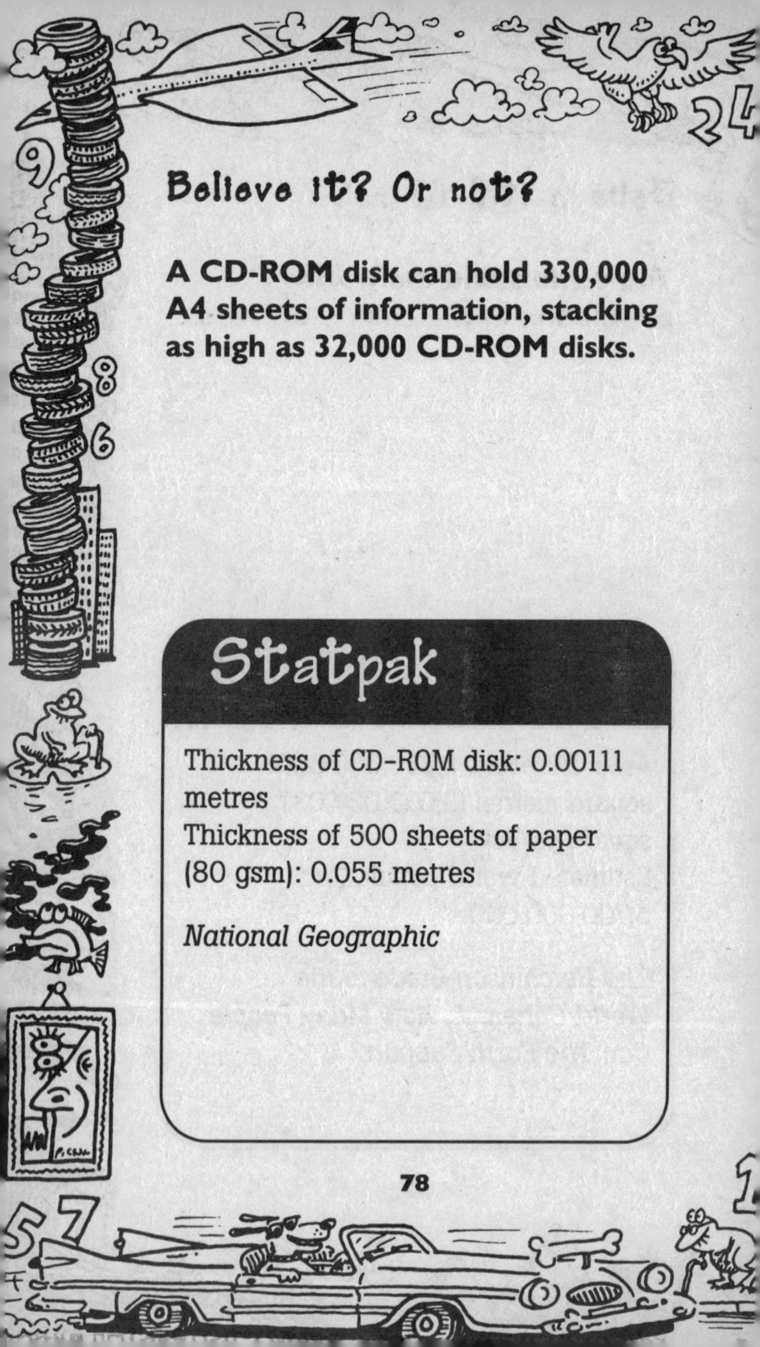

Believe it? Or not?

A CD-ROM disk can hold 330,000 A4 sheets of information, stacking as high as 32,000 CD-ROM disks.

Statpak

Thickness of CD-ROM disk: 0.00111 metres
Thickness of 500 sheets of paper (80 gsm): 0.055 metres

National Geographic

True or false?

A grower could use a different pesticide product every day for over eight years.

Statpak

Number of pesticide products on sale: 3,000
Days in a year: 365

Ministry of Agriculture, Fisheries & Food

Believe it? Or not?

A shopper could change into a different ready-made dress twice a day all year round.

Statpak

Different styles of dress on sale: 777
Days in a year: 365

Drapers Record

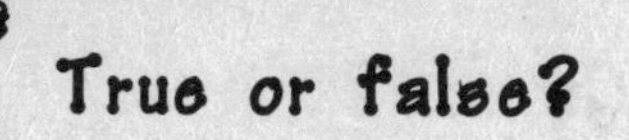

True or false?

Women film directors in Hollywood control the set for only three hours a week.

Statpak

Percentage of Hollywood major release movies directed by women: 5
Hours in a production week: 60

Variety

True or false?

A tourist visiting the USA could ride on a different roller coaster every day for over a year.

Statpak

Roller coasters in the USA: 376
Days in a year: 365

Krantz, L., America By The Numbers

Take your pick

An American bank is being robbed every:

1) week
2) day
3) hour

Statpak

Average bank robberies a year in the USA: 7,500
Days in a year: 365

Federal Bureau of Investigation

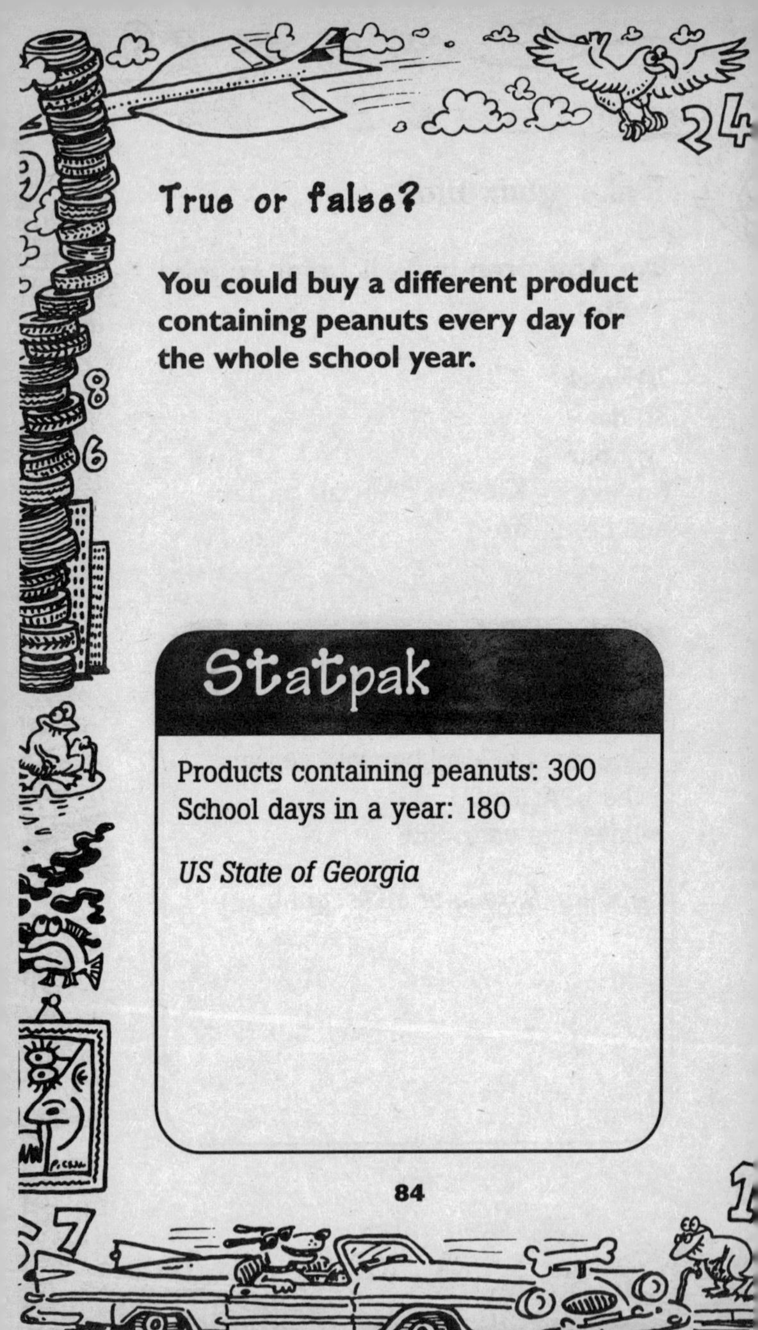

True or false?

You could buy a different product containing peanuts every day for the whole school year.

Statpak

Products containing peanuts: 300
School days in a year: 180

US State of Georgia

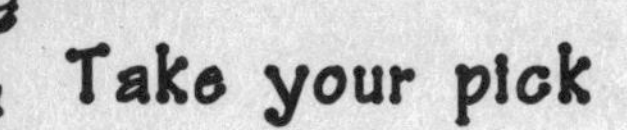

Take your pick

Every second

1) 2
2) 30
3) 358

fingers of Kit-Kat chocolate bar are consumed.

Statpak

Fingers of Kit-Kat bar sold per year: 11,300 million
Days in a year: 365

Nestlé Rowntree

True or false?

Computers sold every year would stack most of the way to the Sky TV satellite.

Statpak

Computers sold per year world-wide: 50,000,000
Height of a computer (monitor on CPU): 0.55 metres
Altitude of Astra satellite: 34,000 kilometres

IEE Spectrum

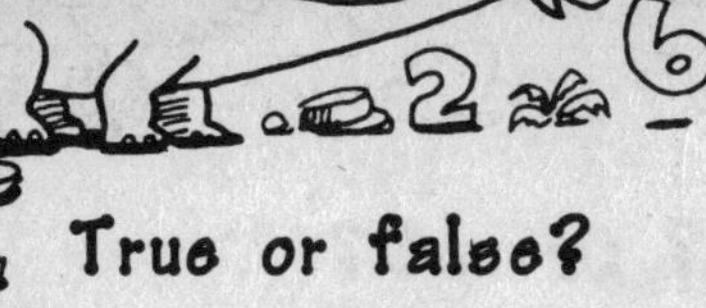

True or false?

Video games can outsell blockbuster movies.

Statpak

First week sales of Mortal Kombat II:
$50 million
First week sales of The Lion King:
$40.87 million

Newsweek

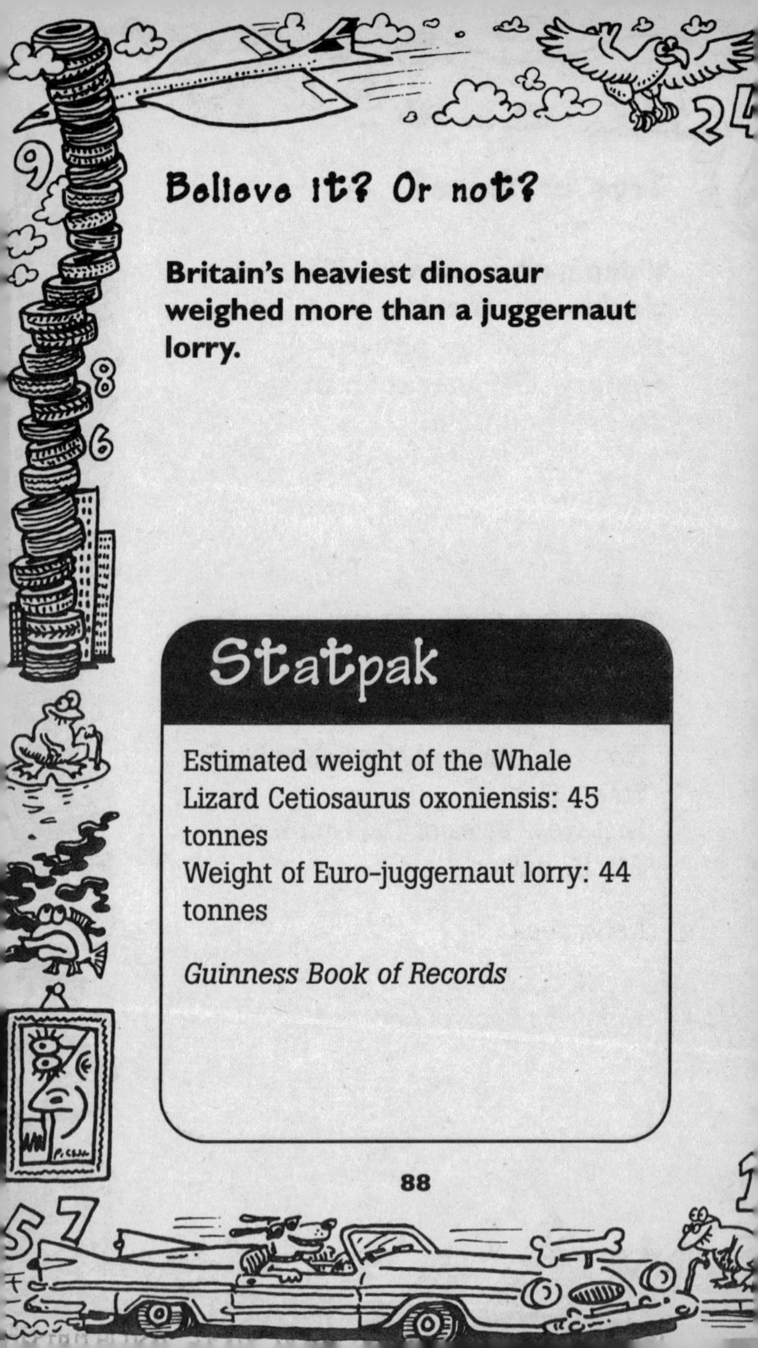

Believe it? Or not?

Britain's heaviest dinosaur weighed more than a juggernaut lorry.

Statpak

Estimated weight of the Whale Lizard Cetiosaurus oxoniensis: 45 tonnes
Weight of Euro-juggernaut lorry: 44 tonnes

Guinness Book of Records

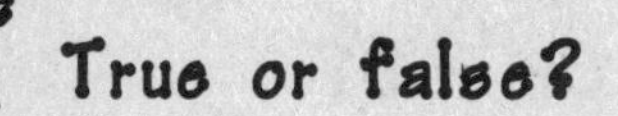

True or false?

If you drew a picture of every different insect on a sheet of paper and stacked the pictures up, they would pile higher than Britain's tallest mountain.

Statpak

Estimated number of species of insect: 30,000,000
Height of 500-sheet pile of paper (80 gsm): 0.055 metres
Height of Ben Nevis: 1,343 metres (4,406 feet)

Guinness Book of Records

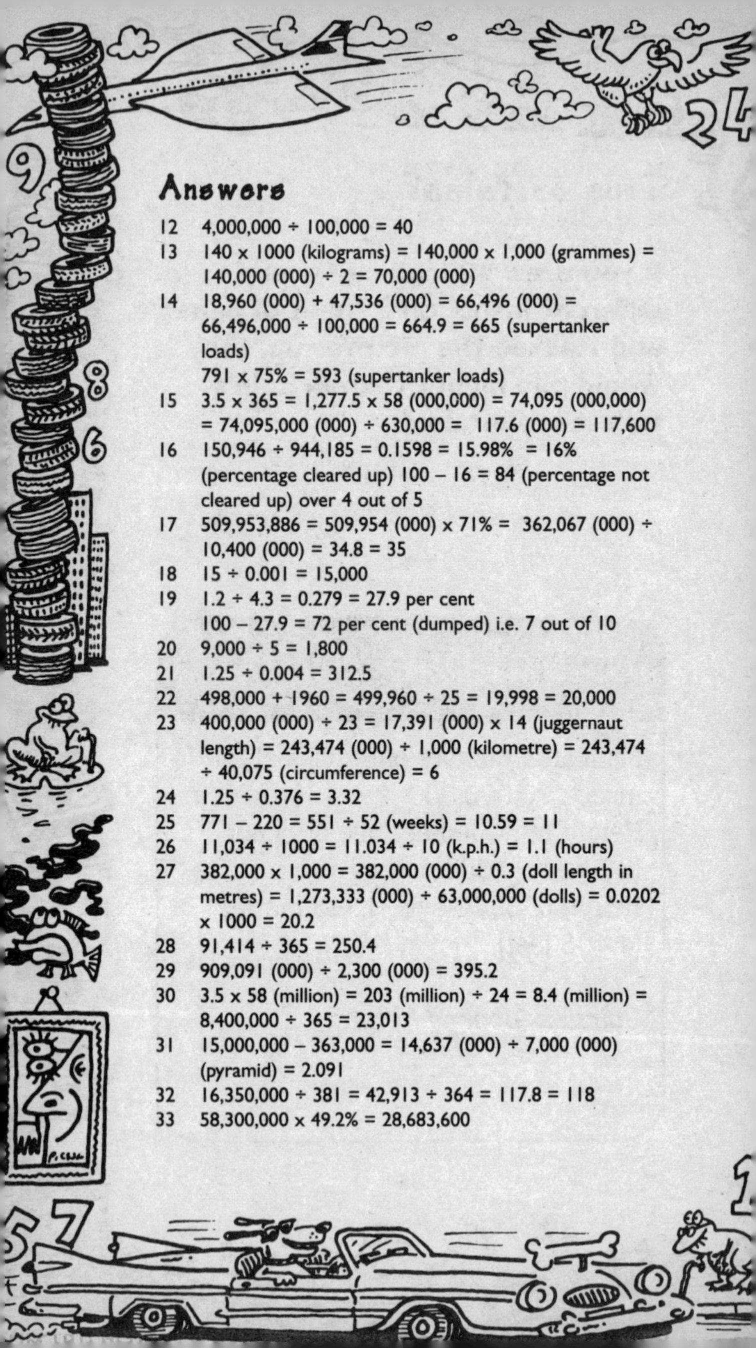

Answers

12 4,000,000 ÷ 100,000 = 40

13 140 x 1000 (kilograms) = 140,000 x 1,000 (grammes) = 140,000 (000) ÷ 2 = 70,000 (000)

14 18,960 (000) + 47,536 (000) = 66,496 (000) = 66,496,000 ÷ 100,000 = 664.9 = 665 (supertanker loads)
791 x 75% = 593 (supertanker loads)

15 3.5 x 365 = 1,277.5 x 58 (000,000) = 74,095 (000,000) = 74,095,000 (000) ÷ 630,000 = 117.6 (000) = 117,600

16 150,946 ÷ 944,185 = 0.1598 = 15.98% = 16% (percentage cleared up) 100 – 16 = 84 (percentage not cleared up) over 4 out of 5

17 509,953,886 = 509,954 (000) x 71% = 362,067 (000) ÷ 10,400 (000) = 34.8 = 35

18 15 ÷ 0.001 = 15,000

19 1.2 ÷ 4.3 = 0.279 = 27.9 per cent
100 – 27.9 = 72 per cent (dumped) i.e. 7 out of 10

20 9,000 ÷ 5 = 1,800

21 1.25 ÷ 0.004 = 312.5

22 498,000 + 1960 = 499,960 ÷ 25 = 19,998 = 20,000

23 400,000 (000) ÷ 23 = 17,391 (000) x 14 (juggernaut length) = 243,474 (000) ÷ 1,000 (kilometre) = 243,474 ÷ 40,075 (circumference) = 6

24 1.25 ÷ 0.376 = 3.32

25 771 – 220 = 551 ÷ 52 (weeks) = 10.59 = 11

26 11,034 ÷ 1000 = 11.034 ÷ 10 (k.p.h.) = 1.1 (hours)

27 382,000 x 1,000 = 382,000 (000) ÷ 0.3 (doll length in metres) = 1,273,333 (000) ÷ 63,000,000 (dolls) = 0.0202 x 1000 = 20.2

28 91,414 ÷ 365 = 250.4

29 909,091 (000) ÷ 2,300 (000) = 395.2

30 3.5 x 58 (million) = 203 (million) ÷ 24 = 8.4 (million) = 8,400,000 ÷ 365 = 23,013

31 15,000,000 – 363,000 = 14,637 (000) ÷ 7,000 (000) (pyramid) = 2.091

32 16,350,000 ÷ 381 = 42,913 ÷ 364 = 117.8 = 118

33 58,300,000 x 49.2% = 28,683,600

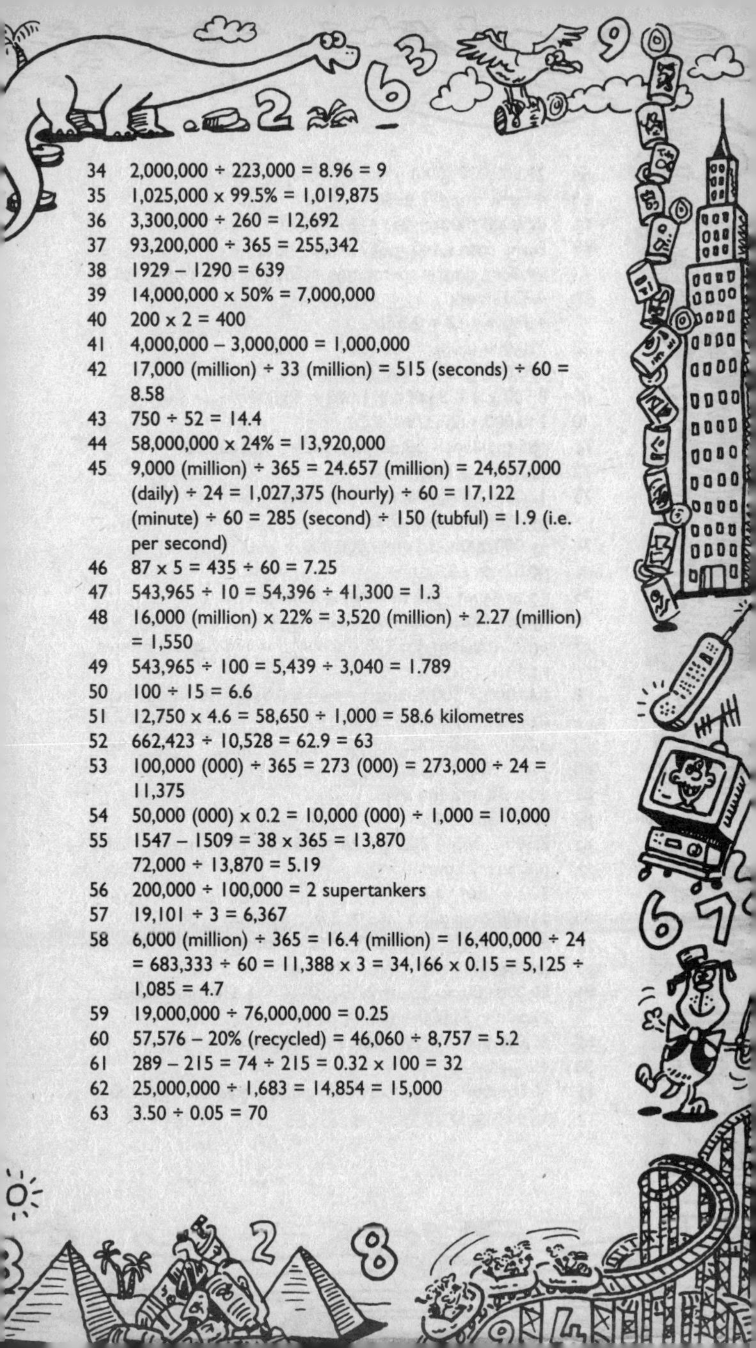

34 2,000,000 ÷ 223,000 = 8.96 = 9
35 1,025,000 x 99.5% = 1,019,875
36 3,300,000 ÷ 260 = 12,692
37 93,200,000 ÷ 365 = 255,342
38 1929 – 1290 = 639
39 14,000,000 x 50% = 7,000,000
40 200 x 2 = 400
41 4,000,000 – 3,000,000 = 1,000,000
42 17,000 (million) ÷ 33 (million) = 515 (seconds) ÷ 60 = 8.58
43 750 ÷ 52 = 14.4
44 58,000,000 x 24% = 13,920,000
45 9,000 (million) ÷ 365 = 24.657 (million) = 24,657,000 (daily) ÷ 24 = 1,027,375 (hourly) ÷ 60 = 17,122 (minute) ÷ 60 = 285 (second) ÷ 150 (tubful) = 1.9 (i.e. per second)
46 87 x 5 = 435 ÷ 60 = 7.25
47 543,965 ÷ 10 = 54,396 ÷ 41,300 = 1.3
48 16,000 (million) x 22% = 3,520 (million) ÷ 2.27 (million) = 1,550
49 543,965 ÷ 100 = 5,439 ÷ 3,040 = 1.789
50 100 ÷ 15 = 6.6
51 12,750 x 4.6 = 58,650 ÷ 1,000 = 58.6 kilometres
52 662,423 ÷ 10,528 = 62.9 = 63
53 100,000 (000) ÷ 365 = 273 (000) = 273,000 ÷ 24 = 11,375
54 50,000 (000) x 0.2 = 10,000 (000) ÷ 1,000 = 10,000
55 1547 – 1509 = 38 x 365 = 13,870
72,000 ÷ 13,870 = 5.19
56 200,000 ÷ 100,000 = 2 supertankers
57 19,101 ÷ 3 = 6,367
58 6,000 (million) ÷ 365 = 16.4 (million) = 16,400,000 ÷ 24 = 683,333 ÷ 60 = 11,388 x 3 = 34,166 x 0.15 = 5,125 ÷ 1,085 = 4.7
59 19,000,000 ÷ 76,000,000 = 0.25
60 57,576 – 20% (recycled) = 46,060 ÷ 8,757 = 5.2
61 289 – 215 = 74 ÷ 215 = 0.32 x 100 = 32
62 25,000,000 ÷ 1,683 = 14,854 = 15,000
63 3.50 ÷ 0.05 = 70

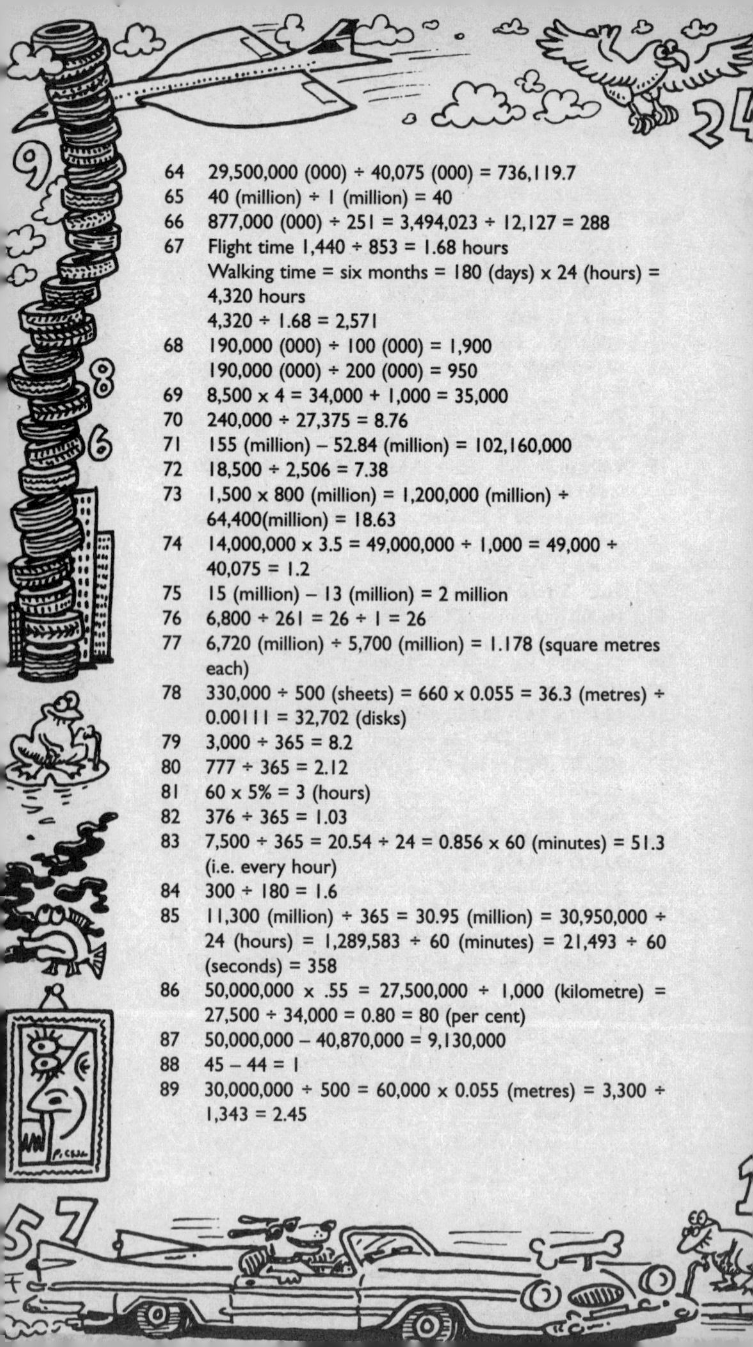

64 29,500,000 (000) ÷ 40,075 (000) = 736,119.7
65 40 (million) ÷ 1 (million) = 40
66 877,000 (000) ÷ 251 = 3,494,023 ÷ 12,127 = 288
67 Flight time 1,440 ÷ 853 = 1.68 hours
Walking time = six months = 180 (days) x 24 (hours) = 4,320 hours
4,320 ÷ 1.68 = 2,571
68 190,000 (000) ÷ 100 (000) = 1,900
190,000 (000) ÷ 200 (000) = 950
69 8,500 x 4 = 34,000 + 1,000 = 35,000
70 240,000 ÷ 27,375 = 8.76
71 155 (million) – 52.84 (million) = 102,160,000
72 18,500 ÷ 2,506 = 7.38
73 1,500 x 800 (million) = 1,200,000 (million) ÷ 64,400(million) = 18.63
74 14,000,000 x 3.5 = 49,000,000 ÷ 1,000 = 49,000 ÷ 40,075 = 1.2
75 15 (million) – 13 (million) = 2 million
76 6,800 ÷ 261 = 26 ÷ 1 = 26
77 6,720 (million) ÷ 5,700 (million) = 1.178 (square metres each)
78 330,000 ÷ 500 (sheets) = 660 x 0.055 = 36.3 (metres) ÷ 0.00111 = 32,702 (disks)
79 3,000 ÷ 365 = 8.2
80 777 ÷ 365 = 2.12
81 60 x 5% = 3 (hours)
82 376 ÷ 365 = 1.03
83 7,500 ÷ 365 = 20.54 ÷ 24 = 0.856 x 60 (minutes) = 51.3 (i.e. every hour)
84 300 ÷ 180 = 1.6
85 11,300 (million) ÷ 365 = 30.95 (million) = 30,950,000 ÷ 24 (hours) = 1,289,583 ÷ 60 (minutes) = 21,493 ÷ 60 (seconds) = 358
86 50,000,000 x .55 = 27,500,000 ÷ 1,000 (kilometre) = 27,500 ÷ 34,000 = 0.80 = 80 (per cent)
87 50,000,000 – 40,870,000 = 9,130,000
88 45 – 44 = 1
89 30,000,000 ÷ 500 = 60,000 x 0.055 (metres) = 3,300 ÷ 1,343 = 2.45